Mathematical
Models
in
Physical Sciences

PRENTICE-HALL INTERNATIONAL, INC. London
PRENTICE-HALL OF AUSTRALIA, PTY., LTD. Sydney
PRENTICE-HALL OF CANADA, LTD. Toronto
PRENTICE-HALL FRANCE, S.A.R.L. Paris
PRENTICE-HALL OF JAPAN, INC. Tokyo
PRENTICE-HALL DE MEXICO, S.A. Mexico City

Mathematical Models in Physical Sciences

Proceedings of the Conference
at the University of Notre Dame, 1962

Conference on Mathematical Models in the Physical Sciences, University of Notre Dame, 1962.

Edited by

Stefan Drobot

Professor of Mathematics
University of Notre Dame

and

PAUL A. VIEBROCK

University of Notre Dame

PRENTICE-HALL, INC.   Englewood Cliffs, N. J.

1/30/64

© 1963 by PRENTICE-HALL, INC., Englewood Cliffs, N.J.
All rights reserved. No part of this book may be reproduced
in any form, by mimeograph or any other means, without per-
mission in writing from the publisher. Library of Congress
Catalog Card Number 63-14982. Printed in the United States
of America. (C)

for chem. Lib.

CHEMISTRY DEPT.

QA
401
C74m

856839

Presented by the Journal of the American Chemical Society 1-22-64

Preface

On April 15-17, 1962, a conference on "Mathematical Models in Physical Sciences" was held at the University of Notre Dame. The conference was sponsored by the National Science Foundation under grant No. NSF-G23332.

I wish to express my appreciation to my graduate assistant, Paul A. Viebrock, whose collaboration in compiling and editing made the publication of these proceedings possible.

Stefan Drobot

Editor

University of Notre Dame

February, 1963

Table
of
Contents

Mathematical
Models
in
Physical Sciences

Formal Opening
of the
Conference

FREDERICK D. ROSSINI
Dean, College of Science
University of Notre Dame

Mr. Chairman and Fellow Professors: on behalf of the University of Notre Dame and of its College of Science, I am very happy to welcome you all to our campus, and to this conference on Mathematical Models in the Physical Sciences.

Today we see good reason for calling Mathematics the Queen of the Sciences. Scientists are encountering innumerable problems that can be solved only by bringing to bear upon them the knowledge and experience and skills of two or more disciplines. Mathematics is a powerful instrument for developing interdisciplinary research because most all phenomena we encounter in the world yield fruitfully to the hard scrutiny of mathematics. The development of scientific discoveries usually follows two stages: one where the sci-

(Copyright © 1963 by Prentice-Hall, Inc.)

1

entist is alone in solitude, meditating and generating the germs of the new ideas; and the other where the scientist is conferring with his fellows, as in the conference here, in discussions which prepare these new ideas for formal presentation by grinding off the rough edges and polishing up the imperfect surfaces.

Your Conference on Mathematical Models in the Physical Sciences involves Physicists and Chemists as well as Mathematicians. And I am sure that many new views will be encountered. We are confident that the results will be most beneficial.

Our very sincere commendation is due Professor Drobot, Professor Steinhaus, and Professor Ross for their work in preparing this Conference. I close with best wishes to you all for a very successful Conference and a pleasant and happy sojourn at Notre Dame.

Microscopic
versus
Macroscopic Models

HAROLD GRAD
Courant Institute of Mathematical Sciences
New York University

We are frequently presented with a situation in which a single physical problem is believed to be representable by two or more distinct mathematical models. Setting aside the motivating physical situation, we are left with two different mathematical structures and a belief that they can be somehow related. Frequently the mathematical connection is made by letting a parameter approach zero in one of the models. When the information that describes a well-posed problem (e.g., boundary or initial data) is different for the two problems, we may expect the limit to be highly singular. Moreover, we can expect the mathematical elucidation of the connection between the two models to be more subtle and more difficult than the theory of either structure alone. In a large class of problems,

(Copyright © 1963 by Prentice-Hall, Inc.)

the transition involves a reduction in the order of a differential system with a concomitant change in the type of equation and in the
number and quality of boundary conditions (Friedrichs, 1955). A
more radical transition may involve a change in the number and
even in the character of the dependent variables in the mathematical structure.

This is the situation when one of the models entails a microscopic description and the other a macroscopic description. We
shall consider three such examples: first the comparison between
the description of a gas using the Boltzmann equation (microscopic)
and the equations of continuum gas dynamics (macroscopic); then
the description of a gas via Liouville's equation (microscopic) and
Boltzmann's equation (macroscopic); finally a sequence of descriptions of a plasma (fully ionized gas) in which one of the descriptions
turns out to be macroscopic with respect to two coordinates and
microscopic in the third. The first example is fairly complete
mathematically (Grad, 1963a, b), the second is only imperfectly so
(Grad, 1958), and the final example is, at the present time, only
formal (Grad, 1961b).

1. KINETIC VS. FLUID DESCRIPTIONS

Two means of describing the behavior of a gas are by means of
a distribution function and the Boltzmann equation on the one hand,
and by means of fluid variables and an appropriate set of partial
differential equations on the other. In the first case one should
specify the distribution function $f(\xi,x)$ initially and the reflected

"half" of the distribution function in terms of the incident "half" at a boundary. For the second, one specifies the fluid state $\rho(x)$, $p(x)$, $u(x)$ initially and, for example, the normal component of velocity at a boundary (inviscid fluid) or the full vector velocity and the temperature (Navier-Stokes equations). Despite the total dissimilarity, one expects the two descriptions to be almost equivalent under appropriate circumstances, roughly that the mean free path and mean free time be small compared to the macroscopic scale of variation.

The appropriate mathematical formulation (Hilbert, 1912) is to place a large factor $1/\varepsilon$ (ε is a scale factor for the mean free path or collision time) before the collision term (a quadratic integral operator) in the Boltzmann equation

$$(1.1) \qquad \frac{\partial f}{\partial t} + \xi \cdot \frac{\partial f}{\partial x} = \frac{1}{\varepsilon} Q[f].$$

Qualitatively, small ε implies small Q, which implies that f is approximately locally Maxwellian ($Q = 0$ implies this rigorously but violates the equation in general). But a local Maxwellian f is equivalent to a fluid description, which establishes a rough connection between the two formulations.

More cautiously, we note that the parameter ε enters singularly into the equation (1.1). Despite this, Hilbert postulates regularity in the form

$$(1.2) \qquad f_H = \sum_0^\infty \varepsilon^n f_n.$$

Inserting this formal power series, we are able to evaluate the successive terms f_n uniquely by an algorithm which requires only the specification of the <u>fluid state</u> initially. In other words, the unwarranted assumption with regard to regularity, (1.2), yields a very special class of solutions with the apparent property that the fluid state is formally causal.

The question arises whether the Hilbert expansion in some sense represents general solutions of the Boltzmann equation, or a very special class of solutions, or possibly none at all. To be precise, let us consider a fixed boundary condition and fixed initial function $f(\xi,x)$ independent of ε; the exact solution of (1.1) will, of course, depend on ε, $f(\xi,x,t; \varepsilon)$. At first glance, the Hilbert expansion appears to yield no information whatever toward an answer since, even though the initial fluid state can be arbitrarily specified (as a power series in ε or not), the initial Hilbert function f_H is necessarily a function of ε. This discrepancy can be resolved, and a satisfactory heuristic answer is obtained (Grad, 1958) by writing (1.1) as an integral equation (with kernel containing ε) and integrating by parts. A power series in ε which is identifiable with Hilbert's is obtained together with a "remainder." Plausible estimation of the remainder yields the conclusion that an appropriately chosen series (1.2) can be expected to be asymptotic to the exact solution $f(\xi,x,t; \varepsilon)$ except in the neighborhood of three regions of nonuniformity:

(1) an initial layer of duration ε,

(2) a boundary layer of thickness ε,

(3) any shock layers which may occur, also of thickness ε.

Evidently the dependence on ε of the Hilbert initial function f_H is required to compensate for the effect of the initial transition layer (during which the power series expansion is invalid) on the ε-independent actual initial f.

Accepting the expansion in ε as likely to be asymptotic, we are faced with three connection problems across the layers of nonuniformity. The first of these, to find the correct initial conditions for the Hilbert theory in terms of an arbitrarily given initial f, has been solved, together with a proof (in the linear case) that the series, when so specified, is indeed asymptotic to the exact solution of the Boltzmann equation (Grad 1963a, b).

The second connection problem, to obtain correct asymptotic boundary conditions for the Hilbert theory to correspond to a boundary condition governing solutions of the Boltzmann equation, remains open. But there seems little doubt that, to first order in ε, the correct Navier-Stokes boundary conditions will be some form of the classical Maxwell "slip" condition. Note that this boundary layer has a scale thickness ε as compared to $\varepsilon^{1/2}$ for the usual viscous boundary layer.

The third connection problem is to generalize the classical Hugoniot jump conditions (which are correct to lowest order for the Euler inviscid fluid equations) as a power series in ε. For example, the presence of a nearby wall (on the scale of the mean free path) will modify the jump conditions across a shock. An approximate treatment of this problem to first order in ε has been made (Probstein and Pan, 1963).

Returning to the initial layer, one can make quite precise the connection between the causality of f based on the Boltzmann equation and the causality of the fluid state in fluid dynamics. First of all, the formal causality of the variables in the Hilbert theory is asymptotically correct, not for the fluid state, but for a certain artificial property of f which, in general, agrees with the fluid state only to leading order in ε. Thus, the Hilbert (also Chapman-Enskog*) theory is salvaged to be quite generally applicable, provided that one applies it to an appropriately chosen modification of the fluid state. Furthermore, by introducing the generalization

(1.3) $f = \exp(-\lambda t/\varepsilon) \sum \varepsilon^n f_n$

of the Hilbert expansion (1.2), where λ takes values from the set of eigenvalues of a certain operator, we obtain a complete sequence of "macroscopic" state variables (the first of which is the modified fluid state), each of which is asymptotically self-causal, and the totality of which is essentially equivalent to f itself. All components except the first (Hilbert) have $\lambda > 0$. In this way, not only the ultimate fluid behavior, but even the details of the initial transient can be studied (asymptotically, for small mean free path) by means of fluid-like partial differential equations.

2. DERIVATION OF THE BOLTZMANN EQUATION FROM PARTICLE DYNAMICS

The problem of the justification of the Boltzmann equation from first principles has long been afflicted with a bad press resulting

*For the distinction between the Hilbert and Chapman-Enskog theories, see Grad, 1958 and 1963a.

from psychological difficulties which are more historical than rational. On the other hand, many derivations that are offered are too naive to relate to the actual substantive difficulties. The reversibility-irreversibility dichotomy presents subtle and formidable mathematical difficulties but not more so than many other difficult (and well-understood) problems involving nonuniform approaches to limits. One important point is that it is possible to approximate arbitrarily closely to an irreversible system with a reversible one and vice versa. Even a single system can exhibit dual features of reversibility and irreversibility depending on the question that is asked; this is associated with the possibility of defining several kinds of entropy function within a fixed dynamical framework (Grad, 1961a). The unifying mathematical concept is the progressive weakening, with the passage of time, of the property of continuous dependence on initial conditions. After a sufficiently long time, a system can develop so severe a loss of memory of its initial state as to appear almost random. For example, to retrace its past history with a given precision, after reversal of all velocities, requires more and more accuracy as time goes on. There are many simple mathematical models which demonstrate this possibility, and this is brought out very elegantly by the spin-echo experiment. In the present context, the irreversible Boltzmann equation is obtained from classical reversible particle dynamics only after a certain limiting process in which many interesting properties retain a finite time scale, but the scale of forgetfulness of other properties becomes infinitesimal (Grad, 1958).

An example which exhibits many of these features but is simple enough to allow mathematical proofs is a gas of noninteracting particles in a rectangular box (the particles collide with the walls but not with one another). It is an elementary exercise to show that any nonsingular initial state will approach uniformity in space after a sufficient lapse of time. There is, of course, no equilibration in velocity space, since the magnitude of each velocity component of every particle is a constant in time. But the distribution function $f(\xi,x,t)$ will converge <u>weakly</u> to the space (and time) independent function

$$(2.1) \qquad F(\xi) = \int f(\xi,x,t)\,dx.$$

Furthermore, the entropy function

$$(2.2) \qquad H = \int f \log f \, d\xi\, dx$$

is constant in time, whereas the entropy

$$(2.3) \qquad H_\rho = \int \rho \log \rho \, dx,$$

involving the spatial density

$$(2.4) \qquad \rho = \int f \, d\xi$$

decreases (but not monotonely) to its minimum value $H_\rho = 0$ at the same time that $\rho(x,t)$ converges to the constant value $\rho = 1$ (Grad, 1961a).

We conjecture that a similar gas of noncolliding particles in a triangular (or tetrahedral) domain will approach uniformity in velocity on the circle $\xi_1^2 + \xi_2^2 = $ constant as well as in space (omitting certain exceptional triangles), but this has not been proved.

We make another plausible conjecture concerning a gas of n

elastic spheres in a box. In the 3n-dimensional space $(x_1, \ldots, x_n)$, the motion is one of constant "speed" $\xi_1^2 + \ldots + \xi_n^2$ on straight line segments which are interrupted by specular reflections at rigid walls $|x_i - x_j| = \sigma$ as well as at the container walls. The evident (weak) limit, for any initial distribution, is one which is uniform on the product of the rather complicated space $(x_1 \ldots x_n)$ and the sphere $\xi_1^2 + \ldots + \xi_n^2 = $ const. If n is large, the limiting velocity distribution of a single particle is approximately Maxwellian (this will be a strong limit). There is an approach to a limit (equilibrium) for any value of n. The limit is approximately Maxwellian if n is large. But this approach to equilibrium cannot be expected to be monotone as predicted by the Boltzmann equation.

To obtain a universal (in some respects monotone) decay toward equilibrium requires a certain limit to be taken which is more than just letting n become large (Grad, 1958). If σ is the diameter of a particle (or a scale factor for the interparticle force more generally), we allow the number density n of particles to increase without bound while shrinking the particles to maintain constant values for $n\sigma^2$ and nm (m is the mass of a particle). Heuristically, we keep the mean free path $(\sim 1/n\sigma^2)$ constant while decreasing the imperfection $(\sim n\sigma^3)$ of the gas. In the limit we obtain a continuum which is a perfect gas and is governed by the Boltzmann equation. The time scale for the evolution of all gas properties which are described by the Boltzmann equation is held fixed in this limit. But the error estimate in the theorem of continuous dependence for the motion of a single particle becomes catastrophically poor. This almost instantaneous loss of memory is the justification for the "Stosszahlansatz" and, when combined with the property of initial chaos (Grad, 1960), yields the universal behavior of the single particle distribution function described by the Boltzmann equation.

On the other side of the coin, this destruction of the conventional estimates of the motion of a particle makes rigorous mathematical proofs exceedingly difficult. It is easily shown that the n-particle distribution function must be allowed to grow exponentially large with n. Also, the temporal evolution of the one-particle distribution for a macroscopically long time is governed by the behavior of the two-particle distribution function on a set of very small measure. We can show that the latter function can misbehave only on sets of small measure. But it is extremely difficult to show that the two small sets do not overlap!

In summary, the radical transfer from properties of Liouville's equation to the Boltzmann equation is accomplished by a similarly radical mathematical limit. The scale of variation of the one-particle distribution must be increasingly large compared to the diameter of a molecule, but can have any fixed relation to the mean free path. As a counter illustration, the formal virial-type expansion suggested by Bogolubov (1946) must be discarded as being incomplete because the required properties cannot follow from the mild limit which is employed. The BBGKY equations couple all multiple distribution functions in an essential way. Of course, in equilibrium, the simple limit n → ∞ is adequate to "synchronize" all distribution functions to the first; even more, to the thermodynamic state. If the macroscopic scale of variation is taken to be large in the BBGKY system, we can expect a similar synchronization with the local thermodynamic state, but this gives a fluid formulation and not a kinetic one like the Boltzmann equation. The question of exactly what limit to take is bypassed by Bogolubov (and many others) by assuming that the higher-order distributions synchronize to the first. This is a logical consequence for a perfect gas (partly proved), but it does not follow at all for a dense gas (Grad, 1958).

Concluding, it is reasonable to expect that although the connection between particle dynamics and the Boltzmann equation is difficult mathematically, it is no more subtle or unexpected than many other nonuniform singular limiting operations.

3. THE GUIDING-CENTER PLASMA

Given the laws governing the motion of a system of particles (e.g., through a Hamiltonian), we can immediately write down a Liouville equation which describes the behavior of a gas of such particles. We then have at our disposal various standard formal approximations which provide a reduction from the highly detailed Liouville equation to a macroscopic fluid formalism. But these procedures can be applied equally well to any well-defined approximation to the laws of motion governing the individual particles, yielding any level of microscopic or macroscopic description for the approximating system of idealized particles.

Consider a gas of charged particles. Using the exact laws of motion in the presence of a given electromagnetic field, we obtain a Liouville's equation including the electromagnetic field as an "external" force field. To complete the description of a collision-less plasma, we include Maxwell's equations for the field in which the charge and current sources are related back to the ion and electron distribution functions. The result is a complicated and nonstandard coupled integro-differential system.

Next we consider the same problem of a collisionless plasma but using the guiding-center approximation to the particle motion; roughly speaking, this requires that the change in electromagnetic field and the energy increment of a particle be small in one gyro (or Larmor) period. The lowest order motion is described most simply by stating that each particle (i.e., its guiding center) is con-strained to lie on a given moving magnetic line (which has the ve-locity $\vec{E} \times \vec{B}/B^2$), with a certain simple Hamiltonian governing the motion along the constraining line; in addition, the spiraling motion about the guiding center is fully described by the statement that the magnetic moment

(3.1) $\mu = \frac{1}{2} m v_\perp^2 / B$

is a constant (this constant μ enters into the Hamiltonian for the guiding-center motion).

Because of the very singular nature of the guiding-center parti-cle motion, the Liouville equation obtained from it, describing a guiding-center plasma (Grad, 1961b) is also very singular. The charge and current source relations of the full theory vanish and reappear as constraints. The motion of the magnetic lines is governed by a macroscopic momentum equation (but, of course, for only the perpendicular component of motion). The Liouville equation describes a one-dimensional gas on each magnetic line. The system is coupled in a very complex way; in particular the gas pressure enters into the equation governing the motion of the lines, and the magnetic field is contained in the Liouville equation. This system, which is microscopic in one dimension and macroscopic in two others, is an exact formal consequence of the postulated guiding-center motion for the individual particles. Further conventional formal approximations yield a fully macroscopic guiding-center fluid. This features a stress tensor with one principle axis parallel to $\vec{B}$ and the other two axes equal (two dimensional isotropy). Thus there are two scalar pressures, and the system is fairly conventional in magneto-fluid dynamics except for an additional equation which can be variously interpreted as perpendicular energy or magnetic moment conservation.

Of course, there is no guarantee that such formal physical or mathematical arguments, no matter how plausible, yield a sensible mathematical structure with reasonable, well-posed problems. Indeed, the guiding-center fluid equations (and probably the plasma equations as well) break down completely and do not allow posing of any initial value problem when the stress tensor is too anisotropic.

They would, presumably, have some physical validity under conditions when they admit solutions at all.

Perhaps the greatest significance of the guiding-center plasma model is that it turns out to be partly macroscopic. Thus there are many important problems in which adherence to a purely microscopic formulation offers no advantage over a macroscopic picture; this despite the much greater computational complexity which results from the detailed pursuit of individual particles.

Both the mathematical and physical significance of the guiding-center fluid and plasma systems remains largely to be discovered.

REFERENCES*

1. N. Bogolubov, J. Phys. USSR **10**, 265 (1946).

2. K. O. Friedrichs, Willard Gibbs lecture, Bull. Am. Math. Soc. **61**, No. 6, 485-504 (1955).

3. Harold Grad
   1958, "Principles of the Kinetic Theory of Gases", in Handbuch der Physik, Vol. XII, Springer-Verlag.
   1960, J. Chem. Phys. **33**, p. 1342.
   1961a, Comm. Pure and Appl. Math. **14**, p. 323.
   1961b, "Microscopic and Macroscopic Models in Plasma Physics" in Proceedings of the Symposium on Electromagnetics and Fluid Dynamics of Gaseous Plasma, Polytechnic Institute of Brooklyn.
   1963a, Phys. Fluids **6**, p. 147.
   1963b, "Asymptotic Theory of the Boltzmann Equation—II", to appear in the Proceedings of the Third International Conference on Rarefied Gases, Paris, 1962.

4. D. Hilbert, Math. Ann. **72**, 562 (1912); also "Grandzüge einer Allgemeinen Theorie der Linearen Integralgleichungen", Chelsea Publ. Co., New York, 1953.

5. R. F. Probstein and Y. S. Pan, "Shock Waves and the Leading Edge Problem", to appear in the Proceedings of the Third International Conference on Rarefied Gases, Paris, 1962.

*More complete references for the material in Sections 1, 2, and 3 are cited in the references, Grad 1963a, 1958, and 1961b, respectively.

Asymptotology*

MARTIN D. KRUSKAL
Plasma Physics Laboratory
Princeton University

When I first saw the program for this conference I was mildly curious about why my talk was scheduled at the end of the first session, following the opening lecture by Professor Grad. Although accepted conference manners (conventional convention conventions, I almost said) forbade inquiring of our genial organizers, I now know the reason—Harold's stimulating and excellent lecture has roused a furor of excitement and even controversy, as they must have foreseen, and it is my function to calm you down, bore you perhaps, and send you off properly soothed and relaxed to enjoy tonight's banquet.

The subject of this conference is unusual, and if I am not at all confident that my chosen topic is entirely appropriate, I am em-

*This work was supported under Contract AT(30-1)-1238 with the Atomic Energy Commission.

(Copyright © 1963 by Prentice-Hall, Inc.)

17

boldened to proceed because of a conviction that it would be out of place anywhere else. But I do feel some trepidation at having Professor Friedrichs in the audience, since I am so heavily indebted to his most enlightening 1955 Gibbs Lecture article,[1] already referred to by Grad.

Asymptotics is the science which deals with such questions as the asymptotic evaluation of integrals, of solutions of differential equations, etc., in various limiting cases. Elements of this science may be learned from the works of van der Corput,[2] Erdélyi,[3] and de Bruijn,[4] and advanced aspects from the numerous references in Friedrichs' cited article. By asymptotology I mean something much broader than asymptotics, but including it; pending further elaboration, I would briefly define asymptotology as the art of dealing with applied mathematical systems in limiting cases.

The first point to note here is that asymptotology is an art, at best a quasi-science, but not a science. Indeed, this explains much of my difficulty both in expounding my material and in finding an appropriate occasion to do so, and it may serve handily to excuse my effort for lacking the high degree of polish which Dean Rossini in his opening remarks assured us we may expect of the presentations (and indeed there does seem to be much Polish about this conference). It explains, too, why I am unable to support the corpus of my dissertation with the hard bones of theorems but must be content with a cartilage of principles, into seven of which I have distilled

whatever of asymptotology I have been able to formulate appropriately and sufficiently succinctly.

The aspect of the definition of asymptotology just given which is
most in need of explanation is the concept of applied mathematical
system. An applied mathematical system is merely the mathematical description of a physical (or occasionally biological or other)
system in which the variables expressing the state of the system
are complete. The importance of formulating problems in terms of
complete state variables constitutes a preliminary principle, not
particularly of asymptotology but of applied mathematics in general, the Principle of Classification (or, perhaps better, of Deter-
minism). It is illustrated by the overpowering tendency, in treating
classical mechanical problems, to enlarge the configuration space
to a phase space, since the phase (configuration together with its
rate of change) but not the configuration alone constitutes a complete description of a classical mechanical system. Consider also
the tendency, in treating probabilistic mechanical problems, to
switch over from this original description, which is incomplete because, for instance, the mechanical "state" at one time does not
determine the "state" at another time, to a new description in
terms of a probability distribution function of the old "states,"
which function evolves "deterministically" in time and is therefore preferable as a state description. This Principle is obviously
closely related to the notion of a well posed problem emphasized by

Hadamard. Its particular relevance to asymptotology comes about because only after one has singled out ("determined") an individual solution (or completely "classified" the family of solutions) can one reasonably inquire into its asymptotic behavior.

Asymptotology is important because the examination of limiting cases seems to be the only satisfactory effective method of proceeding with the analysis of complicated problems (systems) when exact mathematical methods are of no (further) avail (and is often preferable even when they are). It is of value both for obtaining qualitative information (insight) about the behavior of a system and its solutions and for obtaining detailed quantitative (numerical) results. Thus it is hardly surprising that examples, from trivial ones to the most profound, are found everywhere throughout the fields to which analysis (in the technical sense as a branch of mathematics) is applied.

An excellent example of asymptotology is the familiar Hilbert[5] or Chapman-Enskog[6] ("HCE" from now on) theory of a gas described by the Boltzmann equation

(1) $$\frac{\partial f}{\partial t} + \mathbf{v} \cdot \frac{\partial f}{\partial \mathbf{x}} + \mathbf{a} \cdot \frac{\partial f}{\partial \mathbf{v}} = \lambda \int d^3 v \, d\Omega \, |\mathbf{v} - \mathbf{v}'| \, \sigma [\bar{\bar{f}} \bar{f}' - ff']$$

in the limit of high density ($f \to \infty$) or equivalently of frequent collisions ($\lambda \to \infty$), which Grad has already discussed this afternoon. Another example is the Chew-Goldberger-Low[7] theory of the so-called Vlasov[8] system of equations governing an ideal collisionless plasma and its electromagnetic field in what is often called the strong magnetic field (or small gyration radius) limit but is formally best treated[9] as the limit of large particle charges. In the general theory of relativity there is the fundamental Einstein - Infeld - Hoffman[10] derivation of the equation of motion of a "test particle" (one not influencing the space-time metric, i.e., one of negligible mass) by treating it (its world-line, rather) as an appropriate singularity in the metric and letting the strength of the singularity approach zero. Hydrodynamics is rich in asymptotology (theory of shocks as arising in the limit of small viscosity and heat conductivity, theories of strong shocks and of weak shocks, shallow water theory, and so on and on), and so is elasticity. Kirchoff's laws for electrical circuits can be properly derived from Maxwell's equations only by going to the limit of infinitely thin conductors (wires). Simpler examples also abound and are encountered daily by the practicing applied mathematician and theoretical physicist. Naturally it is not practical to discuss deep examples in detail here, so I shall have to confine myself to brief remarks about them, relying for illustration mainly on simple and often trivial instances.

It should now be apparent, I hope, that whatever features such important, wide-spread, and diverse examples may have in common, and whatever lessons for future application may be gleaned from studying them, are well worth formulating and eventually standardizing. Even the many (most? far from all, as I know from my acquaintance) applied mathematicians (etc.) who have become familiar by experience with asymptotological principles, at least in the sense of knowing how to apply them in practice,—even they must inevitably benefit from the introduction of a standard terminology and of the clarity of expression it permits. Implicit knowledge, no matter how widely distributed, deserves explicit formulation, but I am aware of no efforts in this direction which attempt to go anything like so far as I am doing here, though there are some related suggestions in Friedrichs' article.

The final possible obscurity in our previous tentative definition of asymptotology is what it means to deal with a system. To clarify this, we might alternatively define asymptotology as the art of describing the behavior of a specified solution (or family of solutions) of a system in a limiting case. And the answer quite generally has the form of a new system (well posed problem) for the solution to satisfy, although this is sometimes obscured because the new system is so easily solved that one is led directly to the solution without noticing the intermediate step.

To illustrate first by a trivial example, suppose it is desired to follow the (algebraically) largest root x of the simple polynomial equation

(2) $3\varepsilon^2 x^3 + x^2 - \varepsilon x - 4 = 0$

in the limit $\varepsilon \to 0$. There is one root of order ε^{-2} obtained by treating the first two terms as dominant, $x \approx -\frac{1}{3}\varepsilon^{-2}$, for which indeed the other two terms are relatively negligible (even though one of them is absolutely large, of order ε^{-1}), but which is negative. The other two roots are finite, obtained by neglecting the terms with ε factors, $x \approx \pm 2$, the one sought having the plus sign. If we desire it to higher order, incidentally, we may put (2) for this root in the "recursion" form

(3) $$x = 2\left(1 - \frac{3}{4}\varepsilon^2 x^3 + \frac{1}{4}\varepsilon x\right)^{1/2},$$

expand out the right side in powers of ε, and generate better and better approximations for x by continually substituting the previously best approximation into the right side. But this is irrelevant to the present point, which is that (the problem of the algebraically largest root of) the original cubic equation (2) has been replaced by (the problem of the algebraically largest root of) the quadratic equation $x^2 - 4 \approx 0$, or more exactly $x^2 - (4 - 3\varepsilon^2 x^3 + \varepsilon x) = 0$, the quantity in parentheses being treated as known.

In the HCE treatment of system (1) in the limit $\lambda \to \infty$, the original integro-differential equation in the seven independent variables t, $\mathbf{x}$, $\mathbf{v}$ gets replaced by the set of coupled partial differential (hydrodynamic) equations

$$\frac{\partial \rho}{\partial t} \approx -\frac{\partial}{\partial \mathbf{x}} \cdot (\rho\mathbf{u}),$$

(4) $$\frac{\partial \mathbf{u}}{\partial t} + \mathbf{u} \cdot \frac{\partial}{\partial \mathbf{x}}\mathbf{u} \approx -\frac{1}{\rho}\frac{\partial p}{\partial \mathbf{x}},$$

$$\left(\frac{\partial}{\partial t} + \mathbf{u} \cdot \frac{\partial}{\partial \mathbf{x}}\right)(\rho^{-5/3} p) \approx 0$$

in the four independent variables t, **x**; here ρ, **u**, p are of course the usual velocity space moments of f.

These examples clearly illustrate the first asymptotological principle, which is in fact largely the raison d'être of asymptotology. This Principle of Simplification states that an asymptotological (limiting) analysis tends to simplify the system considered. This can occur in at least three general ways.

The basic way systems simplify is merely by the neglect of terms (or, in higher order analyses, at least treatment of small terms as if known, as in the case of the cubic equation earlier). Thus the polynomial equations $x^5 - \varepsilon x + 1 = 0$ and $x^6 + ax^4 + \varepsilon x^3 + 1 = 0$, without getting lower in degree as the cubic did, nevertheless become simple enough in the limit $\varepsilon \to 0$ to be explicitly solvable algebraically. Differential equations in irregular domains approximating regular ones may in the limit become solvable by separation of variables. In other cases the coefficients may become so simple in the limit as to permit solution by Fourier or other transform. These are typical instances of perturbation theory; there are of course also many instances where the simplification which occurs does not appreciably facilitate the further analysis of the system.

A derivative way in which systems simplify, sometimes striking in effect, is the decomposition of the system into two or more independent systems among which the solutions are divided, so that the particular solution of interest satisfies a system with fewer solutions and hence usually in some sense of lower order. Thus the cubic polynomial equation considered earlier split up into a quadratic equation and what is effectively a linear equation. That is, the root of order ε^{-2} was obtained by neglecting the two last terms and writing $3\varepsilon^2 x^3 + x^2 \approx 0$, and though this is cubic it has two trivial unacceptable roots $x \approx 0$ (corresponding to the solutions of the quadratic for finite roots) and is therefore equivalent to the linear equation obtained by dividing through by x^2.

The third (also derivative) way systems simplify, often spectacularly, is through the splitting off of autonomous subsystems. By an autonomous subsystem of a system is meant a part of the system (part of the conditions together with part of the unknowns) which is complete in itself, i.e., forms an applied mathematical system in its own right, so that it can (in principle, at least) be solved before the rest of the system is considered. The qualifier "autonomous" is by no means superfluous. Thus the system $f(x,y) = 0$, $g(x) = 0$ for the two variables x, y has the autonomous subsystem $g(x) = 0$. It has also the nonautonomous subsystem $f(x,y) = 0$ for y, nonautonomous because it is not definite (well-posed) until x has been determined, which requires the other part of the system.

Systems with autonomous subsystems occur much more often than one may at first realize, since there is an instinctive tendency to concentrate attention on the subsystem and forget that it is part

of a larger problem. A particularly contemporaneous illustration
of this is provided by the gravitationally determined motion of the
sun, a planet, and an artificial satellite; the subsystem of the sun
and planet alone is autonomous, since their motions are unaffected
by the satellite and are naturally considered to be given and definite
when its motion is under consideration. But there is a very common special kind of system having autonomous subsystems which
do not get overlooked just because there are too many of them for
any one to be singled out naturally. Such are the initial value problems, which, if well posed for $t_0 < t \leq t_1$ with initial conditions at
t_0, are also well posed for $t_0 < t \leq t_2$ for any t_2 between t_0 and t_1,
so that the autonomous subsystems constitute a continuous one-
parameter family.

For an illustration of the third way of simplifying, note that in
HCE theory the five moments $\rho, \mathbf{u}, p$ satisfy (in the limit, of course)
the autonomous subsystem (4), which is vastly simpler than (1) in
having only four independent variables instead of seven. Similarly
the "general" (for finite ε) pair of simultaneous equations $f(x, y)$
$= 0$, $g(x) + \varepsilon h(x, y) = 0$ reduces for $\varepsilon \rightarrow 0$ to the system with an autonomous subsystem considered earlier. The sun-planet subsystem
split off only by virtue of the implied limit of (relatively) small satellite mass, as is apparent from the less extreme case of the earth
and its natural (rather than artificial) satellite.

The second and third ways both involve a reduction in the number of solutions from which the desired one must be singled out. This is a characteristically asymptotic simplification and, as Friedrichs[1] has affirmed, it justifies the limiting process even though complications arise in other respects. For instance, a linear second order differential equation may reduce to one of first order but nonlinear. The "number" of solutions must be counted in whatever way is appropriate to the instance: as an integer (e.g., for the polynomial equation); as the dimensionality or number of parameters of a family of solutions (as for an ordinary differential equation); as the dimensionality of a parameter space, or number of independent variables of a function characterizing a solution (as with HCE, where seven reduces to four); or what have you.

In carrying out asymptotic approximations to higher order terms we are aided by the (second) Principle of Recursion, which advises us to treat the nondominant terms as if they were known (even though they involve the unknown solution). The simplified system then determines the unknown in terms of itself, but in an insensitive way suitable (in principle at least) for iterative generation of an asymptotic representation of the solution. This has already been illustrated for one of the finite roots of our cubic equation example. For the numerically large root of (2) we may obtain the recursion formula $x = -(x^2 - \varepsilon x - 4)/(3\varepsilon^2 x^2)$. However, this is far from unique; by grouping the terms differently we obtain $x = -(x^2 - 4)/(3\varepsilon^2 x^2 - \varepsilon)$, which is equally suitable, since x has still been solved for from the dominant terms. It would be folly to solve for x from a small term

such as εx; iteration on $x = (3\varepsilon^2 x^3 + x^2 - 4)/\varepsilon$ merely produces

wilder and wilder ε behavior. If one solves from the dominant

terms inappropriately, namely in a way which does not give the so-

lution explicitly outright when the small terms are neglected, then

one has a scheme which may or may not converge, but which, even

if it does, converges at a "finite" rate, not improving the asymp-

totic order of the solution in each iteration. This is illustrated by

putting (2) in the convergent but asymptotically inappropriate re-

cursion form $x = -[-(x^2 - \varepsilon x - 4)/(3\varepsilon^3 x)]^{1/2}$, which is quite usable,

however, for numerical computation.

This trivial example is so trivial that the emphasis on recursion

formulas seems forced. It is true that here and in many, many other

cases one can simply write down an obvious power series in ε and

determine the terms order by order. This approach fails, however,

whenever a more general representation is required, as is by no

means rare. For instance I recently encountered a case where the

obvious series needed to be supplemented by a single logarithmic

term (which was neither the dominant nor even the next-to-dominant

term); the recursion relation generates all the right terms without

prejudice as to their form. Generation of terms by recursion is

often very clumsy for practical purposes, apart from leading to

terms of unexpected form. However, it has a great theoretical ad-

vantage when properties of (all terms of) the series are to be derived, since the recursion relation is highly adapted naturally to the use of mathematical induction. (See the final reference for an example.)

The limiting cases we keep referring to are conventionally, in asymptotics, formulated so as to be cases where a parameter (often denoted by λ) approaches infinity. Since I intend asymptotology to embrace also situations where the limit system itself (not merely arbitrarily near ones) is meaningful (perturbation problems), it is preferable now instead to use a small parameter, conventionally denoted by ε (= $1/\lambda$ for conversion). In fact, it may not be known in advance whether the limit case is meaningful, and, whether or not it is meaningful physically, mathematically it may or may not be so depending on the description employed. This brings us to our third asymptotological principle, the Principle of Interpretation: it is a major task of asymptotological analysis to find variables in which the given problem becomes a perturbation problem (has a meaningful limit situation). This may involve nothing more than recognizing that the original variables are such, as is the case for two roots of the cubic; for the third root, however, the formal limit of (2) is meaningless, but if transformation to the new variable $y = \varepsilon^2 x$ is effected first, the equation obtained for y may be solved by perturbation analysis.

The characteristic feature of asymptotic analyses proper, as opposed to perturbation analyses, is the appearance (in both senses) of overdeterminism. Thus the cubic equation (2) with three roots apparently reduces in the limit to a quadratic with only two; the well behaved (for $\varepsilon \neq 0$) pair of simultaneous linear equations $x + y = 1$, $x + (1 + \varepsilon)y = 0$ formally reduces to a mutually contradictory pair for $\varepsilon = 0$; in the initial value problem $\varepsilon \frac{d}{dt}z + z = 0$ ($t > 0$), $z(0) = 1$, for the continuous function $z(t)$, we seemingly have $z(t) = 0$ in the limit, contradicting the initial condition; and the same thing happens in many less trivial cases (such as the theories of shocks, of boundary layers, and of fast oscillations), as described in detail by Friedrichs.[1] In this connection we have the (fourth) Principle of Wild Behavior, which tells us that apparent overdeterminism arises because (at least some of) the solutions behave wildly in the limit— wildly, that is, compared to our preconceptions, as embodied in the mathematical form of the expressions employed for representing the solutions. Thus in neglecting the cubic (in addition to the linear) term of (3) we have obviously made the implicit assumption that x is not too large (say bounded), which is correct for only two of the roots, while the third behaves "wildly" in becoming infinite (like ε^{-2}); the solution of the simultaneous equations is similarly wild (like ε^{-1}); the solution of the initial value problem, $z = \exp(-t/\varepsilon)$, is wild in having a derivative which, though converging to zero for every fixed positive t, does so nonuniformly and actually becomes infinite for t approaching zero sufficiently rapidly; and similar wildnesses occur in the deeper examples mentioned.

When overdeterminism occurs, if the solution we want is among those still permitted by the formal limit system, well and good: the loss of other solutions is our gain in simplicity (in the second way). If the solution we want is among those lost, then according to the Principle of Wild Behavior we should allow for more general asymptotic behavior of the solution. It is one of the most troublesome difficulties of asymptotological practice to find an appropriate asymptotic form. It is impossible to prescribe a priori all asymptotic representations that may ever prove useful, but among more general representations to try are two worth specific mention as frequently successful. The first is to supplement the originally expected series with new terms, such as smaller (more negative) powers, as in the case of the cubic equation, or logarithmic ones. The second, effective in many of the deeper problems, including those just referred to (see also a detailed example from my own experience[11]), and illustrated by the initial value problem just exhibited (which may in fact be viewed as an elementary boundary layer problem), is to write the unknown as the exponential of a new unknown represented by a series, the dominant term of which must become infinite (at least somewhere) in the limit if anything is to be gained by so doing.

If there can be overdeterminism there can also be underdeterminism, which means that the original well posed problem reduces formally in the limit to a problem with more than one solution. For instance, let A be a known j-by-j matrix, let b and x be j-by-1 matrices, respectively known and unknown, and consider the matrix equation $Ax = b$. Suppose that A and b depend on ε and that the determinant of A is zero if and only if $\varepsilon = 0$. Then the formal lowest order system $A^{(0)}x^{(0)} = b^{(0)}$ is certainly not well posed. Since $A^{(0)}$ is a singular matrix, there exists a 1-by-j matrix n $(\neq 0)$ such that $nA^{(0)} = 0$; for simplicity assume that n is unique (up to a constant factor). If $nb^{(0)} \neq 0$ the limit system obviously has no solution (overdeterminism, as in the previous example of simultaneous linear equations), so assume $nb^{(0)} = 0$. Then $x^{(0)}$ is not completely determined by the limit system, and we have an example of underdeterminism.

Another excellent and rather typical example of underdeterminism is again the HCE problem. Letting $\lambda \to \infty$ in (1) (after dividing through by λ) leads to the information that $f^{(0)}$ is invariant under collisions, i.e. locally Maxwellian in some (local Galilean) coordinate system, which is very far from determining $f^{(0)}$, since there are five parameters (ρ, $\mathbf{u}$, p) needed to specify such a distribution and we are left unprovided with information on how the parameters at different points of space-time are related. (The Chew-Goldberger-Low[7] theory is another such example.[8])

In such straits we are rescued by the (fifth) Principle of Annihilation, which instructs us to find a complete set of annihilators of the terms which persist in the limit, apply them to the original system, and then go to the limit after multiplying by an appropriate function of ε so that the now dominant terms persist in the limit. By an annihilator of a mathematical entity is meant an operator which results in zero when applied to the entity. (Of course there are complicated cases in which this produces only some of the missing information, and the same procedure must be reapplied, perhaps repeatedly.)

In the matrix example, the terms $A^{(0)}x^{(0)}$ and $b^{(0)}$ which persist in the limit are annihilated by multiplication on the left by n. Applying this annihilator to the original equation, dividing by ε, and taking the limit gives what may be written

$$(5) \qquad \lim_{\epsilon=0} \left\{\varepsilon^{-1}n[A - A^{(0)}]\right\} x^{(0)} = \lim_{\epsilon=0} \left\{\varepsilon^{-1}n[b - b^{(0)}]\right\}$$

or $nA^{(1)}x^{(0)} = nb^{(1)}$ if A and b are expandable in integral powers of ε. In the normal case this provides just the one extra condition needed to determine $x^{(0)}$, which by the condition $A^{(0)}x^{(0)} = b^{(0)}$ was determined only up to a solution p of $A^{(0)}p = 0$. In the abnormal case that (5) is not an independent condition, there is a linear combination of $A^{(0)}x^{(0)} = b^{(0)}$ and (5) which gives $0 = 0$. The formation of this linear combination is then our new annihilator, the application of which to Ax = b and $\varepsilon^{-1}n[A - A^{(0)}]x = \varepsilon^{-1}n[b - b^{(0)}]$ leads to a new extra condition which will normally be independent and provide the missing piece of information.

In the HCE problem there are five scalars (mass, three components of momentum, and energy) which are preserved by collisions, so that taking the corresponding moments of (1) annihilates the right side. These are therefore annihilators of the dominant terms, which is why they are applied to (1) to obtain the five hydrodynamic equations relating the values of ρ, $\mathbf{u}$, p (and therefore f which is expressed in terms of them) at different points of space-time.

It is through the application of the Principle of Annihilation that the Principle of Simplification is maintained. The loss of solutions in a limit simplifies a system, while the gain of solutions, or loss of information,* would "complicate" it if we were not able to recover sufficient additional conditions to make up for the information lost.

The basic way systems simplify is by the neglect of terms, as stated earlier. But it commonly happens that the relative asymptotic magnitude of two terms to be compared depends upon some knowledge not yet available or on some assumption or decision not yet made. According to the (sixth) Principle of Maximal Balance (or of Maximal Complication†), for maximal flexibility and generality we should keep both terms, i.e., we should allow for the possibility or assume that they are comparable. In the case of incomplete knowledge this is mere prudence; any term in an equation

---

*Use of this terminology is justified even from the technical viewpoint of information theory, suggesting the possibility of assigning a measure to the decrease in the number of solutions occurring in a limit.

†Partly as a consequence of Professor Friedrichs' comment at the conclusion of my lecture, I now feel that "Minimal Simplification" is more appropriate here.

definitely smaller in order of magnitude than another term may be considered negligible, but no term should be neglected without a good reason. In the case of a pending assumption or decision, the desire to balance two such competing terms helps to determine the choice.

The most widely applicable and hence most informative ordering is that which simplifies the least, maintaining a maximal set of comparable terms. Quite often there is more than one possible maximal set of terms, with no set including all terms of any other. (Sets of terms form a lattice ordered by inclusion.) Each maximal set corresponds to different asymptotic behavior. The solutions may split up according to which behavior they have (second way of simplifying), as with the cubic, or each solution may exhibit a variety of different behaviors, in different regions, as with a boundary layer phenomenon.

For instance in the case of the cubic equation, how could we know that two solutions are finite and one of order ε^{-2}? Put another way, why did we not assume the first and third terms to be the dominant ones, or the second and third, or so on? In this particular case there is an easy answer: if we had, we would have obtained a "solution" for which the neglected terms were not in fact negligible compared to the supposed dominant terms, i.e., the "solution" found would not have been self-consistent. But suppose there were several more terms, would we have had to try every pair? (Or suppose there were two independent small parameters δ and ε instead of only one.) Clearly, no matter which terms are dominant x will behave predominantly as some power of ε. We therefore assume the general representation $x \approx a\varepsilon^q$ and wonder what value of q to take. One might in fact choose arbitrarily any value for q but will then generally find that for finite a only one term of (2) dominates, which is nonsensical, so that $a = \infty$ (if it was the constant term), which is not legitimate, or else $a = 0$ (if it was one of the others), which, if more legitimate, is certainly no more useful. A value of q will only be "proper" if we end up with a representation which is "maximally complicated" in that it really consists of one term $a\varepsilon^q$ instead of "no terms" such as 0 or ∞. If we put $x \approx a\varepsilon^q$ into (2) the successive terms vary as ε to the respective powers $3q + 2$, $2q$, $q + 1$, 0, and it is easy to see that only $q = 0$ or $q = -2$ make two (or more) powers equal minima.

On the side it might be of interest to mention a graphical method of finding the proper values of q which apparently goes back to Newton. It is hardly needed in the present simple illustration but can be a great time-saver in more involved examples (also those of higher dimensionality). We plot each term of (2) as a point on a graph, the abscissa being the exponent of x and the ordinate that of ε (see four heavy points in Figure 1); the coefficient is ignored so long as it is not zero. The specification of a definite relationship between x and ε (i.e. of a definite value of q) leads to the identification of the asymptotic behavior of all terms (present or not) cor-

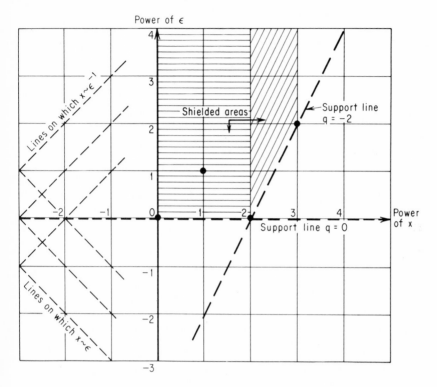

Figure 1

responding to points which are on a common line with a definite slope. Thus, for $x \sim \varepsilon$ all points on the same down-slanting (from left to right) 45° line correspond to a common asymptotic behavior, while for $x \sim \varepsilon^{-1}$ the same holds for up-slanting 45° lines (see dotted lines). Since the smaller the power of ε the larger the term, we seek lines passing through (at least) two graphed points and having no graphed points below them. We may think of finding the lower convex support lines of the set of graphed points, perhaps kinesthetically by imagining pushing a line up from below until it first hits a graphed point and then rotating it around that point until it next hits a second graphed point. It is immediately apparent from Figure 1 that there are just two such lines and that they correspond to q = 0 and q = − 2 (see heavy dashed lines). It is also clear that the point (1, 1), like all points in a semi-infinite vertical strip (see horizontally shaded area), are "shielded" by the points (0, 0) and (2, 0) and can never be on a support line; it is indeed obvious that εx is negligible with respect to either x^2 or 4 no matter how x varies with ε. Similarly there is a semi-infinite vertical strip shielded by the points (2, 0) and (3, 2) (see diagonally shaded area). In more complicated cases we can thus exclude terms wholesale from competition.

To return to our proper business, illustration of the Principle of Maximal Complication, consider the problem of finding the lowest frequency of vibration and the corresponding form of vibration of a uniform membrane stretched between two close wires lying in a plane, one of which we take straight for simplicity. The equation for the standing vibration of a membrane is

(6) $$\frac{\partial^2 u}{\partial x^2} + \frac{\partial^2 u}{\partial y^2} + \nu^2 u = 0,$$

where u is the displacement normal to the (x, y) plane, which is the rest plane of the membrane (the plane containing the wires), and ν is the frequency of vibration of the mode. Let the equations of the wires in the (x, y) plane be y = 0 and y = ε Y(x), where ε of course is the small parameter of closeness. We may suppose $Y(x_1) = Y(x_2)$ = 0 so as to have to consider only the finite region $x_1 < x < x_2$, $0 < y < \varepsilon Y(x)$. Imposing the condition u = 0 on the boundary of this region and (6) inside the region, we have an eigenvalue problem for the lowest eigenvalue ν and its corresponding eigenfunction u. This is one common type of asymptotic problem, asymptotic rather than "perturbational" in that there is no limit problem because the region of interest disappears in the limit. The remedy for this is well known;[1] we rescale the variables appropriately, in this case introducing $\eta \equiv \varepsilon^{-1}y$ so that the region in the (x, η) plane becomes $x_1 < x < x_2, 0 < \eta < Y(x)$, and (6) becomes

$$(7) \qquad \frac{\partial^2 u}{\partial x^2} + \varepsilon^{-2} \frac{\partial^2 u}{\partial \eta^2} + \nu^2 u = 0.$$

Taking the asymptotic behavior of each term at its face value (but remembering that ν is not yet determined), we deem the first term negligible compared to the second, and (by the Principle) assume $\nu^2 \sim \varepsilon^{-2}$ to balance the second and third terms. Introducing $\omega \equiv \varepsilon \nu$ we write (7) as

$$(8) \qquad \frac{\partial^2 u}{\partial \eta^2} + \omega^2 u = -\varepsilon^2 \frac{\partial^2 u}{\partial x^2}.$$

To lowest order we neglect the right side of (8), whereupon x degenerates from an independent variable to a mere parameter. The really proper treatment at this point, by the Principle of Recursion, would be to treat the right side of (8) as known, solve for u on the left in the form of an integral representation (involving the simple,

well known, explicit Green's function), and try to obtain u itera-
tively. Instead we shall do something similar but simpler, more or
less paralleling the lowest order version of the proper treatment.
For each x we have, to lowest order, a simple eigenvalue problem
with the lowest eigenstate $u = A \sin(\pi\eta/Y)$ and eigenvalue $\omega = \pi/Y$.
But ω so defined depends on x, which is impermissible, so we take
$A(x)$ to be a Dirac delta function, the location of whose singularity
we take to be at the maximum of $Y(x)$ in order to have the smallest
ω; for simplicity we assume the maximum of Y to be unique and to
occur at x = 0. In a sense we have now solved the problem originally posed, but since our answer is singular it is not entirely satisfactory (see the next and final Principle to be formulated). Indeed,
since our "solution" is singular in its x dependence, we ought to
worry whether our earlier neglect of $\varepsilon^2 \dfrac{\partial^2 u}{\partial x^2}$ was justified, and we
might well be curious anyway about the true detailed x depend-
ence which we have cavalierly expressed as a delta function. Since
the significant behavior occurs near x = 0 we introduce $\xi = \delta^{-1}x$,
where δ is a small parameter to be determined (related to ε). We
also write $\omega = \omega_0 + \hat{\omega}$, where $\omega_0 = \pi/Y(0)$ and $\hat{\omega}$ is small. Since
$\dfrac{\partial^2 u}{\partial \eta^2} \approx -\pi^2 Y(x)^{-2}u$, from (8) we obtain

$$(9) \qquad \left[\frac{\pi^2}{Y(\delta\xi)^2} - \omega^2\right]A \approx \frac{\varepsilon^2}{\delta^2}\frac{d^2A}{d\xi^2} .$$

Let $Y(\delta\xi) = Y(0) + \dfrac{1}{2}Y''(0)\delta^2\xi^2 + \ldots$ with $Y''(0) < 0$, whereupon this
becomes

(10) $\qquad \left[-\dfrac{\pi^2 Y''(0)}{Y(0)^3} \delta^2 \xi^2 - 2\omega_0 \hat{\omega} \right] A \approx \dfrac{\varepsilon^2}{\delta^2} \dfrac{d^2 A}{d\xi^2}.$

According to the Principle of Maximal Complication we choose the as yet undetermined asymptotic behaviors so as to keep all the terms in the equation and are thus led to take $\delta = \varepsilon^{1/2}$ and $\widetilde{\omega} = \varepsilon^{-1}\hat{\omega}$, obtaining

(11) $\qquad \dfrac{d^2 A}{d\xi^2} + \dfrac{\pi}{Y(0)} \left[\dfrac{\pi Y''(0)}{Y(0)^2} \xi^2 + 2\widetilde{\omega} \right] A \approx 0.$

On the ξ distance scale A must vanish at "infinity," and we have a well known eigenvalue problem arising in the quantum theory of the harmonic oscillator. The lowest eigenfunction is the Gaussian $A = \exp\left\{ -\dfrac{\pi}{2} Y(0)^{-3/2} [-Y''(0)]^{1/2} \xi^2 \right\}$ with real eigenvalue $\widetilde{\omega}$ $= \dfrac{1}{2} [-Y''(0)/Y(0)]^{1/2}$.

Incidentally, if we should be interested in the behavior of u for $|x|$ not very small, where u decreases rapidly, a different procedure must be used. The right side of (8) cannot be neglected there, since $\omega \approx \pi/Y(0)$ does not even approximate the local eigenvalue $\pi/Y(x)$ for which the left side can vanish with $u \neq 0$. The device mentioned earlier of representing the unknown as an exponential works here; with $u = \exp v$, (8) becomes

(12) $\qquad \dfrac{\partial^2 v}{\partial \eta^2} + \left(\dfrac{\partial v}{\partial \eta} \right)^2 + \omega^2 = -\varepsilon^2 \left[\dfrac{\partial^2 v}{\partial x^2} + \left(\dfrac{\partial v}{\partial x} \right)^2 \right].$

We may assume that v is expandable as a series in ε, $v = \varepsilon^{-1}[v^{(0)} + \varepsilon v^{(1)} + ...]$, where the leading term has been taken large of order ε^{-1} to permit the right side of (12) to contribute. We must have

$\dfrac{\partial v^{(0)}}{\partial \eta} = 0$ or the left side will dominate again, so $v^{(0)}$ is a function

of x only, and to dominant terms (12) becomes

$$\frac{\partial^2 v^{(1)}}{\partial \eta^2} + \left(\frac{\partial v^{(1)}}{\partial \eta}\right)^2 + \omega_0^2 = -\left(\frac{\partial v^{(0)}}{\partial x}\right)^2.$$

Viewed as an equation for $v^{(1)}$ this can be linearized and "homo-genized" by reversing the exponentiation procedure, namely by in-troducing $w = \exp v^{(1)}$, whence

$$\frac{\partial^2 w}{\partial \eta^2} + \left[\omega_0^2 + \left(\frac{\partial v^{(0)}}{\partial x}\right)^2\right] w = 0.$$

Together with the boundary conditions on w (that it vanish at $\eta = 0$, $Y(x)$) this is an eigenvalue problem which determines the variation of $v^{(0)}$,

$$\omega_0^2 + \left(\frac{\partial v^{(0)}}{\partial x}\right)^2 = [\pi/Y(x)]^2,$$

as well as the η dependence of w (sinusoidal). All that the device has amounted to in this case, of course, is factoring out (from u) a fast varying function of x, but the use of the exponential represen-tation has led to that procedure in a natural and systematic way.

We complete our list with the simple (seventh) Principle of Mathematical Nonsense: if, in the course of an asymptotological analysis, a mathematically nonsensical expression appears, this in-dicates that the asymptotology has not been done correctly or at least not carried out fully (although even incomplete it may be sat-isfactory for one's purposes). One may come upon expressions such as $0/0$, divergent sums or integrals, singular functions, etc., and whether they are to be considered nonsensical sometimes depends on the use they are to be put to. In the just discussed membrane vibration problem the first instance of mathematical nonsense was the disappearance in the limit of the region over which the partial differential equation was to be solved, the second was perhaps the dependence of ω on x, and the third was the response to this, the use of a singular (delta) function.

Frequent in asymptotological analyses is the occurrence of phenomena on different scales of distance or time. The HCE problem is a well-known case (as Grad has just pointed out), since if f is not prescribed Maxwellian at the initial instant, there is a relatively short period of time (the order of a collision time) during which f becomes Maxwellian, while the five moments remain approximately constant, and a relatively long period (of order λ times as long) during which the five moments (hydrodynamic variables) vary but f maintains its Maxwellian form. For an extremely simple example of the same type, consider the familiar electric circuit equation $V = RI + L\dot{I}$, where the voltage V(t) is an imposed function of time, the current I(t) is to be found, the resistance R and the inductance L are positive constants, and we choose to examine the limit $L \to 0$. Treating $L\dot{I}$ as if it were known, we immediately obtain a recursion formula for I,

(13)
$$I = \frac{1}{R}(V - L\dot{I})$$
$$= \frac{1}{R}\left[V - \frac{L}{R}\dot{V} + \left(\frac{L}{R}\right)^2 \ddot{V} - \left(\frac{L}{R}\right)^3 \dddot{V} + ... \right],$$

which is fine except for not in general satisfying the arbitrary initial condition on I natural for the original first order differential equation. For short times (of order L) $\dot{I}$ is large and V approximately constant, so that the difference of I from its quasi-equilibrium value V/R decays like $\exp(-Rt/L)$; after this transient has died out (13) holds. Incidentally, the expression in brackets in (13) is just like the Taylor expansion in powers of L of V evaluated at the argument $t - L/R$ except for a factor of $(n - 1)!$ in the denominator of the n-th term, which shows that the asymptotic series (13) for I cannot be expected to converge even if V is analytic (which does not stop it from being very useful).

In phenomena with behavior on two different time scales there is a widely pertinent distinction to be observed between finite conservative systems on the one hand and infinite or dissipative systems on the other. For instance, the well-known problem of the harmonic oscillator with slowly varying coefficient of restitution,[12] $\ddot{x} + k(\varepsilon t)x = 0$, is an example of the first kind; on the short (finite) time scale k is approximately constant and the oscillator simply oscillates steadily, while on the long $(\sim\varepsilon^{-1})$ time scale the frequency and amplitude of the oscillation vary in response to the variation in k. Contrast with this the behavior of the dissipative electric circuit, where only initially the current I varies on the short time scale, swooping toward its quasi-steady value. The HCE example shows that a conservative system can act the same way so long as it is infinite; in this case the decay comes about by a process of "phase mixing," and is possible because the Poincaré recurrence time is infinite.

The asymptotic separation of time scales is the basis for an exciting recent approach in statistical mechanics.[13] Typically one obtains equations for the one-particle and the two-particle distribution functions f_1 and f_2 for a gas of appropriate characteristics, and finds that f_1 can vary only slowly, but that f_2 can vary quickly so as to phase-mix towards a quasi-steady distribution as t gets large on the short time scale while remaining small on the long time scale. The limiting distribution f_2 is a functional of f_1, which when substituted into the equation for $\dot{f_1}$ leads to a closed "kinetic equation" for f_1. The irreversibility (timewise) of this kinetic equation comes about in a natural way, in that the limiting f_2 depends on which direction t is taken to the limit (on the short time scale), whether to plus or to minus infinity. It is a major triumph of this approach that the "Stosszahlansatz" can for the first time be actually derived (under moderate smoothness assumptions).

To return to the finite case, I am glad to take the opportunity of advertising a recent paper[14] in which I have elaborately worked out the asymptotic theory of finite systems of ordinary differential equations depending on a small parameter ε which to lowest order have all solutions periodic. Applied to Hamiltonian systems the theory leads to the existence of adiabatic invariants which are constant (integrals) to all orders in ε.

We are all familiar with those rather unsatisfactory research papers in which the author makes a series of largely arbitrary ad hoc approximations throughout, often dubious without (sometimes even with) the author's intuitive grasp of the situation. These "ad-hoaxes" have their place and utility, but how much more desirable and convincing is a properly worked out and elegant asymptotological treatment, with any arbitrary assumptions (like remarkable coincidences in a well constructed mystery story) made openly and aboveboard right at the beginning where anyone can assess their merits for himself, and with the later development unfolding naturally and inexorably once a definite problem and the limit in which it is to be considered have been settled upon!

The art of asymptotology lies partly in choosing fruitful limiting cases to examine—fruitful first in that the system is significantly simplified and second in that the results are qualitatively enlightening or quantitatively descriptive. It is also an art to construct an appropriate generic description for the asymptotic behavior of the solution desired. The scientific element in asymptotology resides in the nonarbitrariness of the asymptotic behavior and of its description, once the limiting case has been decided upon.

Molière has one of his characters observe that for more than forty years he has been talking prose without knowing it. It is doubtful that he benefited from the discovery, but I hope that you will be more fortunate and not disappointed in having by now discovered that asymptotology is what you have been practicing all along!

REFERENCES

1. K. O. Friedrichs, Bull. Amer. Math. Soc. **61**, 485 (1955).

2. van der Corput, references given in Introduction of reference 3.

3. A. Erdélyi, "Asymptotic Expansions," Dover Publ. (1956).

4. N. G. de Bruijn, "Asymptotic Methods in Analysis," North-Holland Publ. (1958).

5. D. Hilbert, Math. Ann. **72**, 562 (1912).

6. S. Chapman and T. G. Cowling, "The Mathematical Theory of Non-uniform Gases," Cambridge [Eng.] Univ. Press (1952).

7. G. Chew, M. Goldberger, and F. Low, Proc. Roy. Soc. **A236**, 112 (1956).

8. A. Vlasov, J. Phys. (U.S.S.R.) **9**, 25 (1945).

9. M. Kruskal, in "La théorie des gaz neutres et ionisés," edited by C. De Witt and J. F. Detoeuf, Hermann, Paris, and John Wiley, New York (1960).

10. A. Einstein, L. Infeld, and B. Hoffman, Ann. Math. **39**, 65 (1938).

11. M. Kruskal, Rendiconti del Terzo Congresso Internazionale sui Fenomeni d'Ionizzazione nei Gas tenuto a Venezia, Società Italiana di Fisica, Milan (1957), same as U.S. Atomic Energy Commission Report No. NYO-7903 (1958).

12. R. Kulsrud, Phys. Rev. **106**, 205 (1957).

13. E. Frieman, J. Math. Phys. (March, 1963), in press.

14. M. Kruskal, J. Math. Phys. **3**, 806 (1962).

DISCUSSION

Friedrichs: I would like to make a few comments concerning the terminology of these various principles. In your "Principle of Maximal Complication" the term "complication" doesn't quite convince me. You want to catch a wild solution. You have to tamper with it. If you tamper too much it tends to something trivial. So you have to make it tame but you have to minimize the tameness.

I wanted to use the term "complication" in connection with the "Principle of Simplification" because so many complications involved in the mathematical formulation of problems in physics are thus due to simplification. For example, if you take a second order equation with ε in front of the second derivative, for which the limit equation for $\varepsilon \to 0$ is of the first order, you don't know whether the boundary condition gets lost, or the new equation is nonlinear; it might have a singularity or the solution may not be single-valued: There are lots of complications. But in spite of this you want to make the simplification. So perhaps you should call this the "Principle of Simplification in Spite of the Resulting Complications."

Kruskal: Obviously all these things require interpretation of the words. It is hard to get labels that are entirely satisfactory.

Models of
Total Ignorance
in Quantum Mechanics

FREEMAN J. DYSON
Institute for Advanced Study
Princeton, New Jersey

1. DEFINITION OF ENSEMBLES

The theory I will talk about is a new kind of statistical mechanics, invented about 10 years ago by Wigner. In ordinary statistical mechanics we assume that we are totally ignorant of the state of a system. We then deduce properties of the system which hold on the average, where the average is defined with respect to a suitably large ensemble of possible states. In the new statistical mechanics we assume that we are ignorant not only of the state of a system, but also of the nature of the system. We then deduce properties which hold on the average, where the average must be defined in terms of an ensemble of systems.

A system is described in quantum mechanics by a finite matrix M operating in a finite vector-space H. We assume that all we

(Copyright © 1963 by Prentice-Hall, Inc.)

know about the system is that it is invariant under some group G of symmetry-operations. The operations g of G will be represented in H by a set of matrices $\Lambda(g)$. The symmetry of the system under G means that M must commute with all the $\Lambda(g)$. It is important that G usually contains the time-reversal symmetry. This means that the $\Lambda(g)$ may be either linear or semi-linear operators in H.

The ensemble of systems is defined as the set of matrices M commuting with $\Lambda(g)$, with a probability-distribution which will be specified in item 3.

2. WEYL THEORY OF GROUP ALGEBRAS

The structure of such an ensemble is determined by a beautiful mathematical theory of Hermann Weyl, to be found in his book "Classical Groups," Chapter 3. The set of all matrices of the form

(1) $\Sigma_g \ a_g \ \Lambda(g)$,

where the a_g are real coefficients, is called the "group algebra" of the group G over the field R of real numbers. This group algebra we call A. The set of matrices M which commute with all matrices in A is called the "commutator algebra" of A, and is denoted by B. There are three main theorems which fix the structure of A and B.

Theorem I. Every group algebra is reducible to a direct sum of irreducible components. An irreducible component is one which cannot be reduced further.

Theorem II. Suppose that A and B are not simultaneously reducible. Then they have the structure

(2) $A = s \, \partial_t$, $B = t \, \partial_s$.

Here s and t are integers, while ∂ is a division algebra, i.e., an algebra in which every non-zero element has an inverse. The notation ∂_t means the algebra of all $(t \times t)$ square matrices with elements in ∂, while $s \, \partial_t$ means the outer product of the algebra ∂_t with an s-rowed identity matrix I_s.

Theorem III. (Frobenius). Over the field R of real numbers, there are only three division algebras, namely

$\partial = R$, real numbers,

$\partial = C$, complex numbers,

$\partial = Q$, real quaternions.

From these three theorems, we conclude that in general the commutator algebra B is a direct sum of irreducible components, each of which has one of the three possible structures R_s, C_s or Q_s.

3. DEFINITION OF MEASURE

The ensemble of matrices in B can be defined in various ways. The one I prefer is to restrict the matrices M to be unitary. The M are also self-dual, that is to say $M = M^D$ where M^D means that we take M transposed with each element conjugated with respect to ∂.

Let B be irreducible. Then the space of unitary M in B can be regarded as a quotient of two groups

(3) $\text{Space} = \dfrac{U(n)}{O(n)}, \quad \dfrac{U(n) \times U(n)}{U(n)}, \quad \dfrac{U(2n)}{Sp(2n)},$

where n is the dimension of B. The three choices in (3) correspond to the three possibilities $\partial = R, C, Q$. The ensemble E is then defined to be the space (3) with a probability-distribution which is the quotient of the invariant group-measures in the numerator and denominator groups.

4. COULOMB GAS ANALOG

Let E be the irreducible ensemble so defined. The eigenvalues of a matrix M in E are n numbers $\exp(i\theta_j)$ distributed around the unit circle. The joint probability distribution for the angles θ_j is

(4) $P(\theta_1, \ldots, \theta_n) = C \prod_{i<j} |\, e^{i\theta_i} - e^{i\theta_j}\,|^{\beta} = e^{-\beta W},$

(5) $W = - \sum_{i<j} \log |\, e^{i\theta_i} - e^{i\theta_j}\,|$

where $\beta = 1, 2$ or 4 for $\partial = R, C$ or Q respectively.

This distribution of the eigenvalues is identical with the distribution of positions of n classical charges free to move on a circular wire, according to the rules of classical mechanics, with repulsive electrostatic forces derived from the potential (5), the temperature being given by

(6) $\beta = (kT)^{-1}.$

The classical Coulomb gas on a circular wire is thus a precise mathematical analog to the eigenvalue distribution in the ensemble E.

5. BROWNIAN MOTION OF EIGENVALUES

Suppose we have not the equilibrium ensemble E but any time-dependent ensemble E(t) defined in the following way. Given a unitary self-dual matrix M at time t, we may write

$$M = VV^D .$$

Then at time $(t + \delta t)$ we have the matrix $(M + \delta M)$ where

$$\delta M = iV\epsilon V^D,$$

and ϵ is a Hermitian self-dual matrix. We assume ϵ to be an infinitesimal random matrix with the invariant second moment

$$\langle \epsilon_{ij} \epsilon_{kl} \rangle = D \, \delta t [\delta_{ik}\delta_{j1} + \delta_{jk}\delta_{i1}].$$

Thus M is executing a Brownian motion with isotropic diffusion controlled by the rate-parameter D.

The effect of this diffusion on the eigenvalues θ_j is given by elementary second-order perturbation theory. We have

$$(7) \qquad \delta\theta_j = \epsilon_{jj} + \sum_k \epsilon_{jk}^2 \left[\frac{1}{2} \cot \frac{1}{2}(\theta_j - \theta_k) \right].$$

From this we deduce the differential equation satisfied by the time-dependent probability-distribution of the angles θ_j

$$(8) \qquad \frac{1}{D} \frac{\partial}{\partial t} P(\theta_1, ..., \theta_n, t) = \sum_j \frac{\partial^2 P}{\partial \theta_j^2} - \beta \sum_j \frac{\partial}{\partial \theta_j} [E(\theta_j)P],$$

$$(9) \qquad E(\theta_j) = - \frac{\partial W}{\partial \theta_j} .$$

This is precisely the Smoluchowski equation describing Brownian Motion of the n-particle Coulomb gas at temperature T and with electric forces $E(\theta_j)$ acting on each particle.

The time-independent solution of (8) is the stationary distribution (4). So we have a very simple and direct proof of (4).

6. GUNSON AND MEHTA IDENTITIES

Mehta Identity. Consider two eigenvalue distributions on the unit circle, one with 2n eigenvalues and $\beta = 1$, one with n eigenvalues and $\beta = 4$. The probability-distribution of the n alternate eigenvalues in the former is identical with the distribution of all eigenvalues in the latter.

Gunson Identity. Consider two eigenvalue distributions on the unit circle. One is a superposition of two uncorrelated sets of n eigenvalues with $\beta = 1$, the other is a single set of n eigenvalues with $\beta = 2$. The distribution of alternate eigenvalues of the former is again identical with the distribution of all eigenvalues of the latter.

These two identities have been proved by algebraic verification. It would be interesting to try to understand them from a deeper point of view, either mathematically or physically.

7. THERMODYNAMICS OF COULOMB GAS

The thermodynamics of the Coulomb gas can be calculated analytically, since we know the partition function

$$\Psi_n(\beta) = \frac{1}{(2\pi)^n} \int \ldots \int_0^{2\pi} \prod_{i<j} | e^{i\theta_i} - e^{i\theta_j} |^\beta \; d\theta_1 \ldots d\theta_n$$

$$= \Gamma\left(1 + \frac{1}{2}n\beta\right) \Big/ \left[\Gamma\left(1 + \frac{1}{2}\beta\right)\right]^n.$$

This formula was proved independently by Gunson and Wilson. Thus the Coulomb gas belongs to the small number of non-trivial many-body systems whose statistical properties are exactly known.

8. MODEL OF AN INCOMPRESSIBLE FLUID

There exists a well-defined limit of the Coulomb gas as $n \to \infty$. This is an infinite gas on a straight wire of infinite length. It has many of the properties of an incompressible fluid, for example the sound-velocity tends to infinity at long wave-lengths. It is, so far as I know, the first example of an incompressible fluid to be derived from a statistical-mechanical model.

In this connection I have a conjecture. Define the sequence of Ursell-Mayer functions as follows

$$T_1(\theta_1) = P_1(\theta_1),$$
$$T_2(\theta_2) = P_2(\theta_1, \theta_2) - P_1(\theta_1)P_1(\theta_2),$$

etc., where P_k means the k-particle distribution-function. Then the identities

$$(10) \qquad \int_{-\infty}^{\infty} T_n(\theta_1, \ldots, \theta_n)d\theta_n = -(n-1)T_{n-1}(\theta_1, \ldots, \theta_{n-1}),$$

certainly hold for the Coulomb gas. They certainly do not hold (even for n = 2) for an ordinary gas with short-range interactions. I con-jecture that for (10) to hold it is necessary and sufficient that the fluid should be macroscopically incompressible. I conjecture this not only in one dimension but also for a three-dimensional fluid.

9. COMPARISON WITH EXPERIMENT

The original purpose of all this theory was to compare it (in the case $\beta = 1$) with observed distributions of energy-levels in heavy nuclei. Heavy nuclei are presumably complicated enough so that a statistical theory ought to be applicable.

The experimental data are usually plotted as a staircase graph, the number $N(E)$ of levels between energy zero and energy E is plotted against E. One way to analyze the data is to make a least-square fit of a straight line to the staircase. The deviation of the level-sequence from uniformity is then measured by the quantity

$$(11) \qquad \Delta^2 = \underset{a,\,b}{\text{Min}} \left\{ \frac{1}{L} \int_0^L [N(E) - aE - b]^2 \, dE \right\}.$$

Here L is the energy-interval which is observed, and $m = N(L)$ is the number of observed levels.

The theory of the Coulomb gas then gives

$$(12) \qquad \Delta^2 = \frac{1}{\pi^2} \left[\log m \pm \frac{1}{2} \right],$$

where the $\pm \frac{1}{2}$ is the statistical scatter to be expected. This shows that the level-series is much more regular than a random sequence of uncorrelated numbers. An uncorrelated sequence would give

$$(13) \qquad \Delta^2 = \frac{1}{15} m.$$

In practice we usually have m about 100, so $(\log m)$ is smaller than m by at least an order of magnitude.

The data are now being analyzed by Mehta and myself. For uranium, we have found $\Delta^2 = 0.8$ instead of the theoretical value

0.4 ± 0.05. It is too soon yet to say whether this is a real disagreement. If it is a true disagreement, we shall have learned something important about the uranium nucleus.

BIBLIOGRAPHY

The substance of this talk is mainly taken from two papers by the author, "The Threefold Way: Algebraic Structure of Symmetry Groups and Ensembles in Quantum Mechanics," and "A Brownian-Motion Model for the Eigenvalues of a Random Matrix." These have meanwhile appeared in J. Math. Phys. **3**, 1191 and 1199 (1962). Some parts of the talk refer to work already published in J. Math. Phys. **3**, 140 (1962), where references to earlier history may be found. Other parts (in particular sections 6 and 9) refer to papers which will appear in J. Math. Phys. **4**, written jointly by Mehta and the author.

DISCUSSION

Dyson: The correlation of eigenvalues (with the experimental data) gives you a rather sharp test of whether the model is any good. Now Mehta, who is in fact responsible for a lot of the theory as well, has calculated the value of Δ^2 for two cases, Uranium 238 and Tantalum 181. These are two cases for which good experiments exist. It turns out in both cases that Δ^2 is larger than the theoretical value. Now, unfortunately, one cannot conclude anything from this. It would be very nice of course if one could definitely show that this model is wrong. But, unfortunately, the value of Δ^2 is very sensitive to even one mistake in the data.

For example, if even one level is missed or if one spurious level is put in, then the staircase is shifted up or down, and it can change Δ^2 by a factor of two or so. So you have to be absolutely sure that your data are complete to make this kind of analysis. So in practice, in this case (U 238) the agreement is quite bad indicating that there are probably several mistakes. And that would not surprise the experimentalists in the least, because many of the levels are really only on the edge of being observable. Some of them are extremely weak.

So the conclusion so far is simply that until we have rather more complete data one probably will not be able to say either that this model is completely wrong or that it is right.

Uhlenbeck: How many levels are involved in the data you have analyzed?

Dyson: Of course we don't go all the way up because the chances of error get larger and larger as you go up, so you cut things off where the data begins to look ragged—I think for U 238 we had 55 levels and for Ta 181 we had 75. It is numbers of that order.

Ulam: But, is it elementary because of the Doppler effect that the levels will overlap? I mean you can't tell precisely how many there are.

Dyson: Well, one hopes that he can in this low energy range. The resolution is exceedingly good, but the real trouble is you do expect

a few extremely weak levels. One can never be sure that you're not

missing some or putting in some which aren't really there.

Uhlenbeck: Why do you take nuclear levels? Why don't you take,

say, the iron spectrum?

Dyson: There are reasons for not taking it. Actually Porter and

Rosenzweig have analyzed the Thorium I spectrum, but the data is

not such good quality as the nuclear data. It's not surprising if you

look at these spectra. There is a certain complementarity problem

because the spectra which are sufficiently complex for this model

to be applicable are not, in general, sufficiently well analyzed.

Grad: How do you determine what is the appropriate data?

Dyson: I could talk for some time about this, but I'd better not. It

turns out that this classification of group algebras which Weyl had

done is essentially identical to the classification of the representa-

tions of Wigner, which you find in his book on group theory. But

Wigner didn't know this and had done the whole thing independently

—so that as far as the physicists are concerned there are three

kinds of representations of groups with semi-linear operations,

and these correspond precisely to these three types of algebra of

Weyl's, and when you're given the group it is rather simple to find

out which representations appear. Of course it would be extremely

nice if you could find an example with $\beta = 4$, because for $\beta = 4$ the

levels repel each other—not linearly—but with the fourth power, so all these effects should be much stronger. I am still looking for a good example of $\beta = 4$.

Mathematically it's very simple. If you take the group G to consist of identity and time reversal with nothing else—no other symmetries—in that case you find $\beta = 1$ for even spin and $\beta = 4$ for half-integer spin. So, if one could find a system in which there is no spatial symmetry but which has odd spin then you would have $\beta = 4$. But experimentally this is somewhat difficult. Unfortunately the rotation group is very good for symmetry properties for nuclei. One could imagine for an atom in a sufficiently complicated medium of unsymmetrical electric fields that one could get this case.

A fact which comes out of all this, which is of some interest, is that in the case of $\beta = 4$—these half-integer spin representations—you can make all your matrices real if you write them in terms of quaternions.

Kac: This lecture cannot end without paraphrasing Thomas Gray's famous saying—When ignorance is bliss it is truly no folly to be wise!

The Mathematical Structure
of the
Bardeen-Cooper-Schrieffer Model*†

RUDOLF HAAG
Department of Physics
University of Illinois

The BCS-model for an infinitely extended superconductor is analyzed mathematically. The reason why the model is solvable becomes evident in the present formulation. It is shown that the
ground states with unsharp particle number belong to irreducible
representations, those with sharp particle number to reducible representations of the basic operator algebra. The connection between
uniqueness of the ground state, irreducibility and linked cluster decomposition is reviewed.

*This research was supported in part by the Office of Naval Research.
†This paper, at the time of its presentation at the Conference, had been submitted to
Il Nuovo Cimento which kindly permitted its reproduction.

(Copyright © 1963 by Prentice-Hall, Inc.)

I. INTRODUCTION

For many questions of interest in the many body problem it is allowable to disregard surface effects and to consider the system under investigation as infinitely extended. One may then expect that it will be advantageous to make use of the idealization (infinite volume, infinite particle number) directly in the formulation of the problem. We shall do this here for the BCS-model.[1]

It is known that this model has the following interesting features (true only for infinite volume):

1) It is exactly solvable.[2]

2) The ground state of the operator $K = H - \mu N$ is degenerate in a sense which is not clearly understood in mathematical terms. A "complete" orthogonal set of ground states can either be labeled by a continuous parameter $0 < \alpha < 2\pi$,[3] or by integers n = 0, ±2, ±4... . The particle number is sharp in the states $|n\rangle$, not sharp in the states $|\alpha\rangle$.

3) The ground states $|\alpha\rangle$, belonging to the first way of labeling, are mathematically simpler to describe than the states $|n\rangle$.

It is the purpose of this note to make these features transparent and to clarify in exactly what sense the ground state is degenerate.

[1]J. Bardeen, L. N. Cooper, J. R. Schrieffer, Phys. Rev. **108**, 1175 (1957).
[2]N. N. Bogoliubov, Physica **26**, 1 (1960).
[3]For this reason B. Zumino ("Werner Heisenberg und die Physik unserer Zeit," Vieweg, Bramschweig, 234 (1961)) suggested the use of a nonseparable Hilbert space in this context. We shall, however, avoid this. Compare theorem a) in section IV below.

II. THE MODEL AND ITS SOLUTIONS

The basic quantities are the operators $\psi_r(\mathbf{x})$, $\psi_r^*(\mathbf{x})$ which satisfy the standard anti-commutation relations

(1) $\{\psi_r(\mathbf{x}), \psi_s(\mathbf{x}')\} = 0; \quad \{\psi_r(\mathbf{x}), \psi_s^*(\mathbf{x}')\} = \delta_{rs}\delta(\mathbf{x} - \mathbf{x}').$

The quantity $\psi_r(\mathbf{x})$ destroys an electron of spin $r(r = 1, 2)$ at the point $\mathbf{x}$ in 3-dimensional space at time $t = 0$; its adjoint creates an electron. Throughout our discussion we shall use only quantities which refer to the same time ($t = 0$).

For mathematical conciseness we shall work with an algebra of bounded operators rather than with the somewhat symbolic quantities $\psi(\mathbf{x})$. This algebra is defined as follows: Take all weighted averages of ψ and ψ^*, i.e., quantities of the form

(2) $\psi(f) = \int \psi(\mathbf{x})f(\mathbf{x})d\mathbf{x}; \quad \psi^*(f) = \int \psi^*(\mathbf{x})f(\mathbf{x})d\mathbf{x}.$

with weight functions f which are square integrable. The collection of these operators we call S. It is well known that, due to the anti-commutation relations (1), these operators are bounded. In fact, their norm square is at most $\int |f|^2 d\mathbf{x}$. If $\int |f|^2 d\mathbf{x} = 1$ then $\psi(f)$ is the destruction operator for a particle with wave function f. Then for any state Φ we have

$\| \psi(f)\Phi \|^2 = \langle \Phi | \psi^*(f^*)\psi(f) | \Phi \rangle \leqslant 1$

because Fermi statistics allows at most one particle with the wave function f.

We define now the algebra R as the von Neumann ring which is generated by S. This means essentially that R consists of all operators which are bounded functions of the operators in S.

From the physical point of view it is good to note that the restriction of square integrability for the weight functions f means that only such observables belong to R which may be measured within an essentially finite region of space ("intensive" quantities). This is a reasonable restriction for the observables. It will become apparent later that certain extensive quantities, which have a vanishing expectation value in the ground state, can also be introduced and that they are unbounded operators which are associated with the algebra R (i.e., their spectral projections belong to R).

The interaction Hamiltonian proposed in ref. 1 for a finite volume V is

$$(3) \qquad H_i(V) = \frac{1}{V} \int \psi_1^*(\mathbf{x})\psi_2^*(\mathbf{x}+\mathbf{z})\psi_2(\mathbf{x}'+\mathbf{z}')\psi_1(\mathbf{x}')v(\mathbf{z},\mathbf{z}')\,d\mathbf{x}d\mathbf{x}'\,d\mathbf{z}d\mathbf{z}'.$$

All integrations are understood to be extended over the volume V. The function $v(\mathbf{z},\mathbf{z}')$, which characterizes the interaction, is supposed to decrease rapidly for large $\mathbf{z}$ or $\mathbf{z}'$. We want to study the spectrum of the operator

$$(4) \qquad K = \lim_{V\to\infty} \int_V d\mathbf{x} \left(\psi_r^*(\mathbf{x})\left(-\frac{\hbar^2}{2m}\Delta - \mu\right)\psi_r(\mathbf{x}) - c\right) + H_i(V).$$

Here V is no longer regarded as the volume in which the system is contained but as a subvolume of the infinitely extended system. The limit $V\to\infty$ is to be understood in the sense of convergence of matrix elements $\langle\psi\,|\,K(V)|\psi\rangle$ for a dense set of states ψ and ψ'. In other words, it is our task to construct a Hilbert space in such a way that these matrix elements have limits as $V \to \infty$ and that the limit matrix may be extended to a self adjoint operator K. The first term in (4) is the kinetic energy. The addition of the second term, in which μ is to be regarded as a given constant (chemical potential), is a convenient standard procedure which forces the particle density in the ground state to a finite value depending on μ. Without this term the ground state would, of course, be the state with zero particles and one would have to prescribe the mean particle density by means of an auxiliary condition to obtain a problem of physical interest. The third term is a c-number constant which has been added to make the eigenvalues of K finite. The unknown constant c has to be adjusted so that the ground state expectation value of K is zero.

We now make the following simple observation:

Lemma: If $Q(x)$ is an even, "quasi-local" quantity, then the space average

$$(5) \qquad \overline{Q} = \lim_{V \to \infty} \frac{1}{V} \int Q(x) dx$$

will commute with all operators of our algebra R.

A typical "quasi-local quantity" is

$$(6) \qquad Q(x) = \int F(z_1 \ldots z_n;\, z_1' \ldots z_m') \psi^*(x + z_1) \ldots$$
$$\psi^*(x + z_n) \psi(x + z_1') \ldots \psi(x + z_m')\, dz_1 \ldots dz_m'.$$

if $F(z,z')$ decreases rapidly for large values of each argument. We call Q even if the total number of Fermi-factors ψ, ψ^* is even.

This lemma is almost obvious but we shall demonstrate it for the case

$$Q(x) = \int F(z_1, z_2)\psi(x + z_1)\psi(x + z_2) dz_1 dz_2.$$

It is sufficient to prove that $\overline{Q}$ commutes with all elements of S. So we calculate

$$[\overline{Q}, \psi^*(f)] = \lim_{v \to \infty} \frac{1}{V} \int F(z_1, z_2)f(y)[\delta(y - x - z_2)\psi(x + z_1)$$

$$- \delta(y - x - z_1)\psi(x + z_2)] dz_1 dz_2 dy = \lim_{v \to \infty} \frac{1}{V} \psi(g)$$

where

$$g(x) = \int F(z_1, z_2)[f(x - z_1 + z_2) - f(x - z_2 + z_1)] dz_1 dz_2.$$

If F decreases sufficiently rapidly for large arguments (and if it is not too singular) then g is square integrable and hence $\psi(g)$ is a bounded operator. Due to the factor $\frac{1}{V}$ we get

(7) $[\overline{Q}, \psi^*(f)] = 0.$

In this section we shall consider only irreducible representations of the algebra R. This means that there shall be no bounded operators in the Hilbert space which do not belong to R. In this case a quantity like $\overline{Q}$ which commutes with all operators in R must be a c-number.

The interaction Hamiltonian does not have the form (5) since it involves two undamped integrations (over x and x') and there is only one factor $\frac{1}{V}$ in front. However, the commutator of H_i with

$\psi(f)$ or $\psi^*(f)$ may be simplified by means of the lemma. For instance

(8) $\quad [H_i, \psi_1(\mathbf{y})] = \lim\limits_{V \to \infty} - \dfrac{1}{V} \int \psi_2^*(\mathbf{y} + \mathbf{z})\psi_2(\mathbf{x}' + \mathbf{z}')\psi_1(\mathbf{x}')$

$\qquad\qquad v(\mathbf{z}, \mathbf{z}')\, d\mathbf{x}'\, d\mathbf{z}'\, d\mathbf{z}$

$\qquad\qquad = -\lim\limits_{V \to \infty} \int d\mathbf{z}' \int d\mathbf{z}\ v(\mathbf{z}, \mathbf{z}')\psi_2^*(\mathbf{y} + \mathbf{z}) \dfrac{1}{V} \int \psi_2(\mathbf{x}' + \mathbf{z}')$

$\qquad\qquad \psi_1(\mathbf{x}')\, d\mathbf{x}'.$

Since $\int v(\mathbf{z}, \mathbf{z}')\psi_2^*(\mathbf{y} + \mathbf{z})\, d\mathbf{z}$ is a bounded operator for every value of $\mathbf{z}'$ the norm of which goes to zero for large $|\mathbf{z}'|$ we can, in an irreducible representation, replace the last factor in (8) by a c-number function $\varphi(\mathbf{z}')$ and obtain

$$[H_i, \psi_i(\mathbf{y})] = -\int \Delta(\mathbf{z})\, \psi_2^*(\mathbf{y} + \mathbf{z})\, d\mathbf{z}$$

with

(9) $\quad \Delta(\mathbf{z}) = \int v(\mathbf{z}, \mathbf{z}')\, \varphi(\mathbf{z}')\, d\mathbf{z}'.$

Similarly, one works out the commutators of H_i with $\psi_2, \psi_1^*, \psi_2^*$ and finds that the result is always linear in ψ or ψ^* (for an irreducible representation). This means that under these circumstances H_i may be replaced by the bilinear expression

(10) $\quad H_i' = \int (\Delta(\mathbf{z})\psi_1^*(\mathbf{x})\psi_2^*(\mathbf{x} + \mathbf{z}) + \Delta^*(\mathbf{z})\psi_2(\mathbf{x} + \mathbf{z})\psi_1(\mathbf{x}))\, d\mathbf{x}d\mathbf{z} + C.$

Let us denote the result of the substitution of H_i' instead of H_i into (4) by K'. Since K' is a bilinear expression in ψ and ψ^*, it can easily be diagonalized by means of the Bogoliubov transformation.

We get

(11) $\quad K' = \int E(\mathbf{p})(\gamma_1^*(\mathbf{p})\, \gamma_1(\mathbf{p}) + \gamma_2^*(\mathbf{p})\, \gamma_2(\mathbf{p}))\, d\mathbf{p}$

where γ_r, γ_r^* is a system of Fermi operators satisfying the same anticommutation relations as ψ_r, ψ_r^* and

(12) $E(\mathbf{p}) = [\epsilon^2(\mathbf{p}) + |\widetilde{\Delta}(\mathbf{p})|^2]^{1/2}$; $\epsilon = \dfrac{\mathbf{p}^2}{2m} - \mu$.

Here $\widetilde{\Delta}(\mathbf{p})$ is the Fourier transform of $\Delta(\mathbf{x})$. The relation between the ψ-operators and the γ-operators is given by

(13) $\psi_1(\mathbf{p}) = u(\mathbf{p})\gamma_1(\mathbf{p}) - v^*(\mathbf{p})\gamma_2^*(-\mathbf{p})$

         $\psi_2(\mathbf{p}) = v^*(-\mathbf{p})\gamma_1^*(-\mathbf{p}) + u(-\mathbf{p})\gamma_2(\mathbf{p})$

with

(14) $u(\mathbf{p}) = \dfrac{\widetilde{\Delta}}{\left[(E - \epsilon)^2 + |\widetilde{\Delta}|^2\right]^{1/2}}$; $v(\mathbf{p}) = \dfrac{E - \epsilon}{\left[(E - \epsilon)^2 + |\widetilde{\Delta}|^2\right]^{1/2}}$

Obviously K' has a unique ground state which is invariant under translations and characterized by

(15) $\gamma_r(\mathbf{p})\Psi_0 = 0$ for $r = 1, 2$ and all $\mathbf{p}$.

The unknown additive constants in K' have been fixed in (11) by the requirement that the lowest eigenvalue shall be zero. Using the translational invariance of Ψ_0 we can sharpen our lemma to the following statement: In an irreducible representation the space average of a quasi-local quantity is a c-number and is equal to the ground state expectation value:

(16) $\overline{Q} = \lim \dfrac{1}{V} \int_v Q(\mathbf{x})\,d\mathbf{x} = \langle \Psi_0 \mid Q(\mathbf{x}) \mid \Psi_0 \rangle$

The solution depends on the still unknown function $\varphi(z)$. According to (16) we have

(17) $\varphi(\mathbf{z}) = \langle \Psi_0 \mid \psi_2(\mathbf{z})\,\psi_1(0) \mid \Psi_0 \rangle$

which can be evaluated with the help of (13), (15). We find for the Fourier transform of φ,

(18) $\varphi(\mathbf{p}) = -u(\mathbf{p})v^*(p)$.

If we insert the expressions (14) for u and v and (9) for Δ we get the integral equation which determines φ ("gap equation"). It is well known that, for suitably attractive potential, this equation has several solutions. There is the trivial solution $\varphi = 0$, and a one-parametric manifold of non trivial ones

(19) $\varphi_\alpha(\mathbf{z}) = e^{i\alpha}\varphi_0(\mathbf{z})$

where φ_0 is a real function. For each of these solutions we can evaluate the "energy density" c, see equation (4), from the condition

(20) $\langle \Psi_0 | K | \Psi_0 \rangle = 0$

using (13) and (15). It is lower for the nontrivial solutions than for the trivial one which means that we must reject the latter. It is, however, independent of the value of α. Indeed the value of α is irrelevant for all physical consequences. It enters only in the ground state expectation values of those products of ψ, ψ^* which have a different number of starred and unstarred factors. Every observable has an equal number of starred and unstarred factors and hence an expectation value which is independent of α. From the mathematical point of view, however, we have for each value of α a different (inequivalent) representation of our operator algebra R. This means the following: For each value of α we have a Hilbert space $\mathcal{K}_\alpha$ which is generated from the ground state (which we shall call $\Psi_0(\alpha)$) by repeated application of the γ^*. The definition of the γ^* in terms of the ψ, ψ^* contains, of course, the angle α. In each of these spaces the ground state expectation values of the elements of the algebra R are known and, except for those elements of R which are observables, they depend on α. The space $\mathcal{K}_\alpha$ cannot be mapped onto $\mathcal{K}_{\alpha'}$ in an isometric way such that $Q^{(\alpha)}$ (the representative operator in $\mathcal{K}_\alpha$ of the element Q of the algebra) goes over into $Q^{(\alpha')}$. For, if that were possible, then $\Psi_0^{(\alpha)}$ would be mapped into a vector Φ in $\mathcal{K}_\alpha$, for which

$$\langle \Phi \mid Q^{(\alpha')} \mid \Phi \rangle = \langle \Psi_0^{(\alpha)} \mid Q^{(\alpha)} \mid \Psi_0^{(\alpha)} \rangle \quad \text{for all Q in R.}$$

This would imply that Φ must be translationally invariant and different from $\Psi_0^{(\alpha')}$. The latter is, however, the only translationally invariant state in $\mathcal{K}_{\alpha'}$.

We can now answer one of the questions raised in the introduction: "Degeneracy of the ground state" means, for a system of infinitely many degrees of freedom, that the Hamiltonian allows several inequivalent irreducible representations of the basic algebra. The connection between the form of the Hamiltonian and the representation of the canonical commutator algebra has been studied for some Bose-Field models by F. Coester and R. Haag,[4] and by H. Araki.[5] In these models the representation was uniquely determined by the Hamiltonian.

[4] F. Coester and R. Haag, Phys. Rev. 117, 1137 (1960).
[5] H. Araki, Journal of Math. Physics, 1, 492 (1960).

As in ordinary quantum mechanics one may expect that the degeneracy is connected with a symmetry property of the theory. In the BCS-model it is the gauge invariance (of first kind) of K. The substitution

(21) $\psi \rightarrow \psi e^{i\beta}$; $\psi^* = \psi^* e^{-i\beta}$

brings the representation in $\mathcal{K}_\alpha$ over into that in $\mathcal{K}_{\alpha + 2\beta}$. In the case of infinite volume this substitution cannot be replaced by a unitary transformation. (Inequivalence of the representations).

We note that due to our lemma, the irreducibility condition forces us to replace the original gauge invariant operator K by K' which is not gauge invariant. That is, the irreducibility condition has the same effect as Bogoliubov's small symmetry destroying perturbation.

III. STATES WITH "SHARP PARTICLE NUMBER"

In a system with an infinite number of degrees of freedom there are two convenient ways of characterizing a state. The first one, adopted in the preceding section, Eq. (15), specifies the set of annihilation operators of the state. The second possibility is to specify the expectation values of all elements of R in the state. This amounts to giving the functions

(22) $W(\mathbf{x}_1 ... \mathbf{x}_n; \mathbf{y}_1 ... \mathbf{y}_m) = \langle \Phi | \psi^*(\mathbf{x}_1) ... \psi^*(\mathbf{x}_n) \psi(\mathbf{y}_1) ... \psi(\mathbf{y}_m) | \Phi \rangle$

For each of the states $\psi_0^{(\alpha)}$ (which we will denote from now on by $|\alpha\rangle$) these functions are sums of products of the three basic two point functions

$$\langle \alpha \,|\, \psi_2(\mathbf{x} + \mathbf{z}) \psi_1(\mathbf{x}) \,|\, \alpha \rangle = \varphi(\mathbf{z})$$

(23) $$\langle \alpha \,|\, \psi_1^*(\mathbf{x}) \psi_2^*(\mathbf{x} + \mathbf{z}) \,|\, \alpha \rangle = \varphi^*(\mathbf{z})$$

$$\langle \alpha \,|\, \psi_r(\mathbf{x}) \psi_s^*(\mathbf{x} + \mathbf{z}) \,|\, \alpha \rangle = \delta_{rs} \chi(\mathbf{z}).$$

A state with a sharp particle number is one for which the expectation value of any non gauge invariant quantity vanishes. We define therefore the state $|\Omega\rangle$ by

(24) $$W_\Omega(\mathbf{x}_1 \,..\, \mathbf{x}_n; \mathbf{y}_1 \,..\, \mathbf{y}_m) \equiv \langle \Omega \,|\, \psi^*(\mathbf{x}_1) \,..\, \psi^*(\mathbf{x}_n) \psi(\mathbf{y}_1) \,..\, \psi(\mathbf{y}_m) \,|\, \Omega \rangle$$

$$= \begin{cases} \langle \alpha \,|\, \psi^*(\mathbf{x}_1) \,..\, \psi^*(\mathbf{x}_n) \psi(\mathbf{y}_1) \,..\, \psi(\mathbf{y}_m) \,|\, \alpha \rangle & \text{for } n = m \\ 0 & \text{for } n \neq m. \end{cases}$$

The right hand side is independent of the value of α (since $n = m$). One checks the positivity condition

(25) $$\langle \Omega \,|\, Q^\dagger Q \,|\, \Omega \rangle \geqslant 0 \quad \text{for every } Q \text{ from } R.$$

This is the only necessary condition which the w-functions have to satisfy in order to describe a state. We see further that $|\Omega\rangle$ is translationally invariant and that it leads to the same energy density as the states $|\alpha\rangle$.

We consider now the Hilbert space $\mathcal{H}_\Omega$ which results from the application of the algebra R on $|\Omega\rangle$. We claim that in $\mathcal{H}_\Omega$ the operator

(26) $$U = \varphi_0^*(\mathbf{z})^{-1} \lim \frac{1}{V} \int \psi_1^*(\mathbf{x}) \psi_2^*(\mathbf{x} + z) \, d\mathbf{x}$$

is unitary and independent of $\mathbf{z}$. It commutes with all elements of R but is not a c-number.

Proof. We already know that U commutes with R. (Lemma in section II). To see that it is not a c-number we form

(27) $\quad |\Omega_2\rangle = U |\Omega\rangle.$

With the help of (24) we find that $|\Omega_2\rangle$ is a vector with unit length which is orthogonal to $|\Omega\rangle$, since

(28) $\quad \langle \Omega | \psi^* \psi^* | \Omega \rangle = 0.$

Using the detailed form of the W-functions as sums of products of two point functions we check that the matrix elements of U are independent of the value of z and that

(29) $\quad \langle \Omega | Q' U^\dagger UQ | \Omega \rangle = \langle \Omega | Q' Q | \Omega \rangle = \langle \Omega | Q' UU^\dagger Q | \Omega \rangle$

for every pair of operators Q', Q from R. This proves the unitarity.

We have, therefore, in $\mathcal{H}_\Omega$ a whole string of orthogonal vectors

(30) $\quad |\Omega_{2n}\rangle = U^n |\Omega\rangle; \quad n = 0, \pm 1; \pm 2 \ldots.$

which are all translationally invariant. All these vectors describe the same physical state since the expectation values of the elements of R are identical in all of them. The operator, whose eigenvalues distinguish the different n-values, is not contained in the algebra R. This operator would measure the "difference in particle number" between the various $|\Omega_n\rangle$. The fact that this quantity cannot be constructed in any way from the ψ and ψ^* may be illustrated by the following futile attempts:

$$N = \int \psi^* \psi \, d\mathbf{x} = \infty;$$

$$N - \bar{N} = \int (\psi^*(\mathbf{x})\psi(\mathbf{x}) - \langle \Omega | \psi^*(\mathbf{x})\psi(\mathbf{x}) | \Omega \rangle) \, d\mathbf{x} = 0 \quad \text{on every } |\Omega_n\rangle.$$

$$\bar{\bar{N}} = \lim \frac{1}{V} \int \psi^* \psi \, d\mathbf{x} = \text{c-number in } \mathcal{H}_\Omega.$$

If we want to split $\mathcal{H}_\Omega$ into subspaces which are invariant under R we have to diagonalize the operator U which commutes with R.

From the preceding section we know already that the possible ei-
genvalues of U are $\varphi_\alpha^*(\mathbf{z})/\varphi_0^*(\mathbf{z}) = e^{-i\alpha}$, $(0 < \alpha < 2\pi)$. In other words,
U has continuous spectrum. Its eigenvectors will be improper (non
normalizable) elements of $\mathcal{K}_\Omega$. The "differential subspace" of $\mathcal{K}_\Omega$
belonging to the eigenvalue α is the space of the preceding section.
Of course, one can obtain the same result directly, writing down the
eigenvalue problem

(31) $U\Phi = \lambda\Phi.$

For a translationally invariant state Φ we can expand in terms of
the $|\Omega_n\rangle$ and use $U|\Omega_n\rangle = |\Omega_{n+2}\rangle$ to solve (31).

   To close this section let us compare the situation described
above with that of a "normal" Fermi system in which the ground
state is, for instance, the Fermi sea. For a finite volume we can,
in each case, define the ground state (or degenerate ground states)
for each particle number. The possible degeneracy there is irrelevant to our problem and arises in the case of the Fermi sea, for instance, from the different possibilities of placing the last particles
in the various momentum cells which have equal absolute value of
$\mathbf{p}$. We shall therefore not distinguish these degenerate ground
states for a finite system and use the symbol $|N\rangle$ for any one of
them. In the normal case

(32) $\langle N + 2 |\psi^*(\mathbf{x})\psi^*(\mathbf{y})|N\rangle \to 0$

if the volume is increased and N/V held fixed. This means that for
$V \to \infty$ all the states $N + n$ (n any finite number) coalesce. There
remains a single ground state for any given value of the density. In

the BCS-case the limit of (32) is different from zero. While, phys-
ically, the states $|N\rangle$, $|N + 2\rangle$, etc., also are indistinguishable in the
limit by any reasonable measurement, they would have to be repre-
sented mathematically by different vectors in one Hilbert space. In
this case one can get a Hilbert space with a unique ground state
only by taking suitable superpositions of the states $|N\rangle$.

IV. CONNECTION BETWEEN IRREDUCIBILITY, UNIQUENESS OF GROUND STATE AND LINKED CLUSTER DECOMPOSITION

Within the framework of Lorentz invariant, local field theories it
has recently been shown that any one of the three properties i) irreducibility, ii) uniqueness of the vacuum, iii) linked cluster decomposition of vacuum expectation values implies the two others.[6,7,8]
This connection holds true to some extent also for non relativistic
field theories such as, for instance, the many body problem in an
infinite volume. The BCS-model is a beautiful illustration.

The discussion is independent of the specific model and uses
only a few general properties. We are not interested here in obtaining the strongest possible results from the weakest possible
assumptions and therefore the argument will be much less deep
than that in refs. 6 and 7.

Let us call a "homogeneous state" a normalizable vector which
is invariant under translations in space. We assume that there is
at least one such vector (say $|\Omega\rangle$) in the Hilbert space $\mathcal{H}$ and that

[6]H. Borchers, preprint, On the Structure of the Algebra of Field Operators.
[7]D. Ruelle, preprint, On the Asymptotic Condition in Quantum Field Theory.
[8]K. Hepp, R. Jost. D. Ruelle, and D. Steinmann, Helv. Phys. Acta. **34**, 542 (1961).

$\mathcal{H}$ is the space which results if one applies the algebra R on the vector $|\Omega\rangle$ and completes.

Under these assumptions the following may be said:

a) $\mathcal{H}$ is separable.

b) If $\mathcal{H}$ is irreducible with respect to R then $|\Omega\rangle$ is the only homogeneous state.

c) If $\mathcal{H}$ is reducible there must either be several homogeneous states or the momentum operator $\vec{P}$ cannot be associated with R. The latter alternative would mean that the linear momentum of the system cannot be expressed in terms of the basic quantities ψ, ψ^*. In the field-theoretic discussion of refs. 6 and 7 it is shown that this alternative can be excluded by virtue of the restriction of the energy-momentum spectrum to the positive cone.

d) Let $Q(x), Q'(x)$ be two quasi-local quantities. Then the asymptotic decomposition

$$(33) \qquad \lim_{a \to \infty} \langle \Omega | Q(\mathbf{x} + \mathbf{a}) Q'(\mathbf{y}) | \Omega \rangle = \langle \Omega | Q(\mathbf{x}) | \Omega \rangle \langle \Omega | Q'(\mathbf{y}) | \Omega \rangle$$

is true exactly if $|\Omega\rangle$ is the only discrete eigenstate of the momentum. The property (33) is a very weak form of the linked cluster decomposition property of ground state expectation values. We do not say how fast the limit is approached as a function of $\mathbf{a}$, nor shall we consider here the case of more than two clusters, i.e., expectation values, of $Q_1(\mathbf{x} + \mathbf{a}_1)$ $Q_2(\mathbf{x} + \mathbf{a}_2)$ ... $Q_n(\mathbf{x} + \mathbf{a}_n)$ where $a_1..a_n$ all become large in different directions.

e) If we have rotational invariance then a discrete eigenstate of the momentum must be a homogeneous state.

For the proof of a) we refer to refs. 6 and 7. It is essentially a consequence of the fact that the manifold $R|\Omega\rangle$ has (topologically) the same structure as the Fock space of quantum field theory.

To prove b) let us suppose there were a second homogeneous state, say $|\Omega'\rangle$, in $\mathcal{K}$. According to the construction of $\mathcal{K}$ the matrix elements

$$(34) \qquad \langle \Omega' | \psi^*(\mathbf{x}_1) \ldots \psi^*(\mathbf{x}_n) \psi(\mathbf{y}_1) \ldots \psi(\mathbf{y}_m) | \Omega \rangle = M(\mathbf{x}_1, \mathbf{y}_m)$$

cannot vanish for all values of n and m. In fact, we can assume that M is non zero for some even value of n + m. It vanishes for odd values of n + m if we can appeal to the superselection rule which operates between states with an even number of Fermions and those with an odd number. Denoting an operator with a non vanishing matrix element (34) by Q and using the translational invariance of $|\Omega'\rangle$ and $|\Omega\rangle$ we see that

$$M = \langle \Omega' | Q | \Omega \rangle = \langle \Omega' | \lim \frac{1}{V} \int_v Q(\mathbf{x}) \, d\mathbf{x} | \Omega \rangle;$$

where $Q(\mathbf{x}) = e^{-i\mathbf{Px}} Q \, e^{i\mathbf{Px}}$.

According to the lemma in section II, the operator $\lim(1/V)\int Q(\mathbf{x})d\mathbf{x}$ commutes with all elements of R. If $|\Omega'\rangle$ differs from $|\Omega\rangle$ this operator cannot be a c-number. Hence the representation is reducible.

To prove c) we note that if $\mathcal{K}$ is reducible then there is a nontrivial operator X which commutes with R.

We have

$$X|\Omega\rangle = |\Omega'\rangle \neq \lambda|\Omega\rangle$$

because if $|\Omega'\rangle$ were parallel to $|\Omega\rangle$ then also

$$XR|\Omega\rangle = RX|\Omega\rangle = \lambda R|\Omega\rangle$$

for the whole algebra R and hence X would be λ times the identity in the whole Hilbert space. Now, if the momentum operator $\vec{P}$ is associated with R, then also

$$[X, \vec{P}] = 0.$$

This would imply that $|\Omega'\rangle$ is again a homogeneous state. Thus we have the alternative described under c).

The proof of statement d) is given in ref. 8. We can write the left hand side of (33) as

$$\langle\Omega|Q(\mathbf{x}) e^{i\vec{P}\mathbf{a}} Q'(\mathbf{y})|\Omega\rangle.$$

For large **a** this expression approaches

$$\sum \langle\Omega|Q(\mathbf{x})|n\rangle\langle n|Q'(\mathbf{y})|\Omega\rangle \exp^{i P_n \mathbf{a}}$$

where the sum extends only over the discrete eigenstates of **P**. If there is only one such state, namely $|\Omega\rangle$, then we have (33). Otherwise not.

The statement e) follows from a) if we have rotational invariance. If **p** is in the spectrum of the operator **P** then all the **p**' which are obtained from **p** by a rotation must be in the spectrum. Therefore, $\mathbf{p} \neq 0$ cannot be a discrete eigenvalue or else we would have a continuous manifold of normalizable, orthogonal states, i.e., a nonseparable Hilbert space in contradiction to a). So the only allowed discrete eigenvalue of **p** is zero.

Acknowledgment. It is a pleasure to thank B. Mühlschlegel, Th. Maris and B. Schroer for many discussions and R. Schrieffer for a censureship of the manuscript.

DISCUSSION

Case: What is the thing which prevents the linked-cluster property from telling you as much as the irreducibility? I mean what is the analog of Schur's lemma?

Haag: That is a good question. There is a connection between the uniqueness of the ground state and the linked-cluster property. If you have translational invariance you can say the following: Take a quasi-local operator $Q(x)$ and a quasi-local operator $Q(y)$ and consider

$$\langle \Omega \,|\, Q(x)\, Q(y)\,|\, \Omega \rangle$$

for large distances $|x - y|$. What happens? Well, we can replace $Q(y)$ by

$$e^{-i\mathbf{P}\,\mathbf{y}}\, Q(0)\, e^{i\mathbf{P}\,\mathbf{y}}.$$

This is just translating from 0 to the point y. If Ω is translation invariant then

$$e^{i\mathbf{P}\,\mathbf{y}}\,|\,\Omega \rangle = |\,\Omega \rangle.$$

What we are really calculating here is the matrix element of $e^{-i\mathbf{P}\,\mathbf{y}}$ between some state $Q(0)\,|\,\Omega \rangle$ and some other state $Q(x)\,|\,\Omega \rangle$ for large y.

Suppose we take a sum over a complete set of intermediate states

$$\langle \Omega \mid Q(x) \mid N \rangle \langle N \mid e^{iPy} Q(0) \mid \Omega \rangle.$$

How does a large translation act on a fixed state? If you analyze the vector $\mid N \rangle$ according to eigenstates of the momentum operator you get the sum,

$$\sum C_n e^{iP_n y}.$$

If N is not in the discrete spectrum then you have an integral over dp, and for very large y this oscillates very rapidly. Then by the lemma of Riemann and Lebesque this vanishes. (Only in the discrete case do you have a non-vanishing contribution.) So you would say in such a situation that asymptotically, for large y, only those components with discrete eigenvalues will survive.

Now if you have uniqueness of the ground state—if you have only one discrete eigenstate of the momentum—only one exactly translationally invariant state, then you can replace

$$\langle \Omega \mid Q(x) \mid N \rangle \langle N \mid e^{iPy} Q(0) \mid \Omega \rangle$$

by

$$\langle \Omega \mid Q(x) \mid \Omega \rangle \langle \Omega \mid Q(0) \mid \Omega \rangle,$$

so you get the linked cluster property

$$\langle \Omega \mid Q(x) Q(y) \mid \Omega \rangle \rightarrow \langle \Omega \mid Q(x) \mid \Omega \rangle \langle \Omega \mid Q(y) \mid \Omega \rangle.$$

If you have more than one invariant state then you do not have the linked-cluster property but you have a sum over all discrete eigenstates of the momentum instead. So if you want the linked-cluster property it means that you can have only one normalizable, translationally-invariant state.

Is this what you wanted to know?

Case: No, you haven't come to the point. I want to know what the analog of Schur's lemma is.

Haag: The criterium for irreducibility is Schur's lemma itself which states that any quantity which commutes with all operators must be a multiple of the identity. Since we want to consider here a Hilbert space which is irreducible with respect to the collection of "Quasilocal" operators, we have to use in Schur's lemma only quasilocal operators instead of arbitrary functions of the fields.

Friedrichs: I would like to ask one question concerning what your notion of sharp particle number is. They refer to the ψ-particles, don't they? So they refer to what are called "bare" particles, which is apparently meaningful here. So if you select a definite H, a definite particle, then you don't have a sharp particle number. Why, and what, do you call sharp?

Haag: Well I call the particle number sharp when the functions

$$\langle \Omega \,|\, \psi^*(\mathbf{x}_1) \dots \psi^*(\mathbf{x}_n)\psi(\mathbf{y}_1) \dots \psi(\mathbf{y}_n) \,|\, \Omega \rangle$$

are zero, except for m = n of course. That is, if the particle number is sharp, then if I create 5 particles and destroy 3, I must have a vanishing expectation value because I have changed the particle number. So I take as the definition of sharp particle number in a state that the expectation values are all zero except for m = n.

Friedrichs: You do not say a definite number of particles.

Haag: No, that number is infinite anyhow. You would have to consider the difference between infinite and infinite plus two etc. You cannot express an operator which makes such a distinction in terms of the psi's.

Friedrichs: What else do you have instead?

Haag: This is the reason why the space which has states with sharp particle number is not irreducible. There are other operators in it which you cannot express in terms of the psi's.

Uhlenbeck: Do you think that this degeneracy of the ground state which the BCS theory gives is essential to super conductivity?

Haag: Unfortunately I am not educated about super conductivity.

Uhlenbeck: I mean, at the moment, that this stuff still seems accidental to me.

Haag: Let me put it this way. If you think that it is essential for the explanation of some effects of super conductivity that you have a pairing of electrons, you can imagine, loosely speaking, the system to be made up of bound states of pairs of electrons which are correlated in the sense that you have a square integrable wave function, so that in some respect you have a gas of bound electron pairs.

Uhlenbeck: Couldn't it just be correlated?

Haag: If you think you can get away with unbound correlation you don't need the degeneracy. If you need them to be really bound then you get this degeneracy.

Dyson: How come you are not talking about a realistic super conductor anymore, but you take a charged bose gas which will also give you super conductivity?

Haag: You mean bose condensation?

Dyson: Yes. Does this have this property or not?

Haag: The bose condensation has exactly the same property.

Uhlenbeck: I don't like this ordinary bose gas because the interest for me lies in the irreducibility and gauge invariance. I would like to ask the same question for the charged bose gas.

Haag: Well, you have the same phenomenon which I discussed here for the BCS-model already in the case of an uncharged bose gas, namely the "breaking of an invariance" which was present in the basic equations. This invariance corresponds to the conservation of particle number and can formally be expressed as a "gauge invariance of the first kind" which means that one multiplies all destruction operators by a phase factor and all creation operators by the inverse phase factor.

Uhlenbeck: What about the electro-magnetic field?

Haag: That is a stronger kind of gauge invariance, the "gauge invariance of the second kind".

Some Properties
of Certain Non-Linear
Transformations

STANISLAW M. ULAM
University of California
Los Alamos Scientific Laboratory

Several of the papers presented at this meeting dealt with new developments in linear theories in quantum theory. Professor Dyson's lecture especially showed how far one can push the ideas of linear representations—the applications he made of the theory of operators constitute a real triumph of the economy of these ideas. In several other talks there were, however, allusions to non-linear transformations which may be necessary in a future fundamental physical theory.

Very little is known about non-linear transformations, even simple ones, e.g., quadratic transformations in vector spaces, even in the finite dimensional ones. In this talk a brief account will be given of some experimental work concerning certain special non-

(Copyright © 1963 by Prentice-Hall, Inc.)

linear transformations and their asymptotic or ergodic properties. This work was done jointly with Paul Stein and was possible because of the use of the fast computing machines and I shall present some of the observations made in these studies. Mathematics is not really an observational science and not even an experimental one. Nevertheless, the computations which were performed were useful in establishing some rather curious facts about simple mathematical objects.

To plunge into medias res: The transformations studied were of the type illustrated by the example

$$X' = 2XY + 2XZ + 2YZ$$
$$Y' = X^2 + Z^2$$
$$Z' = Y^2.$$

Here X, Y, Z are real numbers between 0 and 1 and their sum is 1. The new variables X', Y', and Z' will be also in this range and their sum will be also 1. This transformation, in the three-dimensional space, of a convex set into itself is an example of a more general type: we expand $(X + Y + Z)^2$, divide the six binomial terms into three classes—arbitrarily—and have, it turns out, 91 different types of quadratic transformations. (These are all distinct even under permutation of letters.) The interpretation or motivation for this special type of transformations is, for example, the following: Suppose X, Y, Z denote fractions, in a population which is assumed to be very large, of three different types of particles. We might call them blue, red, and green particles. We assume that these mate in pairs at random and each pair produces two offspring whose color is determined by the colors of the parents. For example, in the transformation given above, the X-type together with Y-type give an X-type, so do X with Z and Y with Z. Mating X with its own type and mating Z with its type give the Y type. Mating Y with itself gives type Z. The expected number of particles of each color in the next generation will be then given by the formulae above. If one wants to compute the fractions of the population of each of the three types in the next generation, one will iterate the transformation.

In general, as time goes on by discrete generations, the fractions will be given by the successive iterates of our transformation. One may be interested, among other properties, in the asymptotic behavior of the fractions of the population of each type. It turns out that for some transformations of this type the iterates of almost every point converge to a unique fixed point of the transformation. This means that asymptotically the population becomes stable and a "steady state" is approached. For certain other transformations, still of this type, the fixed point is repulsive and instead of converging to a fixed point, the iterates of a point might converge to a periodic configuration. The period might be for example of order 3; for a transformation of this type in four variables, we found convergence to a period of order 12. For some other transformations but still of this type, the asymptotic or limiting configuration might not be a finite set of points and this limiting set can have a very peculiar structure. A full account of this work is given in a

Los Alamos Report No. LA-2305 where the case of three variables
was studied exhaustively.

The main part of this talk is concerned with cubic transformations in three variables. (Strictly speaking, since the sum of the
variables is equal to 1, the transformation is then in two variables.)
There the examples studied are still of this form: we take $(X + Y + Z)^3$. We obtain 10 binomial terms which we divide as before into
three classes. Setting X' equal to one group of terms, Y' to the
other, and Z' to the remaining, we obtain an example of the transformations we have studied. Here the limiting set may exhibit a

Figure A. The limiting set of points under the iteration of the transformation:

$$x_1' = x_1^2 + x_3^2 + 2x_1x_2$$
$$x_2' = 2x_1x_3 + 2x_2x_4 + 2x_3x_4$$
$$x_3' = x_2^2 + 2x_2x_3$$
$$x_4' = x_4^2 + 2x_1x_4$$
$$x_1' + x_2' + x_3' + x_4' = x_1 + x_2 + x_3 + x_4 = 1$$

The view is a projection of the 3-dimensional set, the three straight line
segments serve merely as an indication of the orientation of the coordinate axes in space.

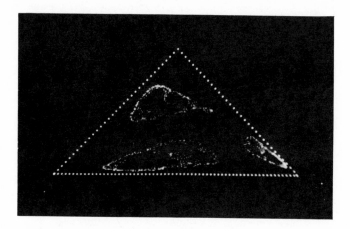

Figure B. The limiting set of points for the transformation:

$$x_1' = x_2^3 + 3x_1x_2^2 + 3x_2x_1^2 + 3x_3x_2^2$$

$$x_2' = 3x_1x_2^2 + 3x_3x_1^2 + 6x_1x_2x_3$$

$$x_3' = x_1^3 + x_3^3 \qquad (x_1 + x_2 + x_3 = x_1' + x_2' + x_3' = 1)$$

The triangle shown is the boundary of the region which is being transformed into itself.

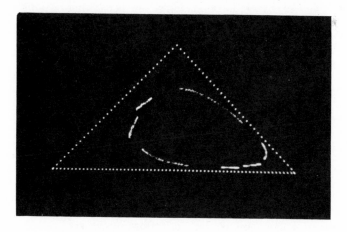

Figure C. The limiting set of points for the transformation:

$$x_1' = x_3^3 + 3x_1x_2^2 + 3x_2x_3^2 + 3x_3x_2^2 + 6x_1x_2x_3$$

$$x_2' = 3x_1x_3^2 + 3x_3x_1^2$$

$$x_3' = x_1^3 + x_2^3$$

$$(x_1 + x_2 + x_3 = x_1' + x_2' + x_3' = 1)$$

great pathology in many cases. In some it consists of a set of points which is infinite but nowhere dense. In other cases it gives the appearance of a curve, in some others still, finite periods of very high order seem to be the limiting configuration. For these cubic transformations, however, it is also true that in the majority of cases there is a convergence to a fixed point. If this is not the case, then the limiting set may depend on the initial starting point but there are regions within the domain of definition such that no matter with which point in the region one starts, the limiting set will be the same.

The computing work was facilitated by a device which displayed visually the iterated points—hundreds or thousands of them—on a screen and photographed the result. One might look upon our study as providing some orientation about the behavior of simple algebraic non-linear transformations which occur in problems analogous to the one studied by Volterra on symbiosis of several types of species and, more generally, in biological—genetic problems. A detailed account of this work with Paul Stein will appear as a Los Alamos Report. In a different context, the study of such transformations can serve as a preparation for the study of some non-linear generalizations of the Schrödinger equation. C. J. Everett and the writer have considered the following:

In the most simple and naive case consider the time independent Schrödinger equation:

$$\Delta\psi + [E - V(x, y, z)]\psi = 0$$

where V is a given function of position (defined on the configuration space). E is an eigenvalue to be determined. One requires the solution to be integrable over the whole space of its definition. There might be boundary conditions other than square integrability; for example, the function sought should vanish at prescribed places, etc.

This equation can be studied in the form

$$\frac{\partial u}{\partial t} = \Delta u - V \cdot u$$

where $u(x, y, z, t)$ of four variables and t is a re-introduced parameter enabling one to omit an explicit mention of E: for large values of t the solution u, one can prove, will have the asymptotic form

$$u(x, y, z, t) = e^{-Et} \psi(x, y, z)$$

where ψ is independent of t and will satisfy the first equation.

In problems of nuclear physics and in the attempted theories of elementary particles, V may not be easily determined or "given." Some time ago, it was proposed to consider—somewhat in the spirit of field theories with "self-consistent" equations—instead of a given potential another unknown function whose square, that is to say its probability density, would serve as a potential for the function ψ. This unknown function would itself obey a differential equation similar to the first equation above. We would then have a system of linked equations, the solution of each serving as a "potential" for the other.

(1)
$$\frac{\partial u}{\partial t} = \Delta u + a_1(v^2) \cdot u + b_1(u^2)u + \cdots$$

$$\frac{\partial v}{\partial t} = \Delta v + a_2(u^2) \cdot v + b_2(v^2)v + \cdots$$

We have considered as the most elementary case a system of equations

(2)
$$\frac{\partial u}{\partial t} = \Delta u + v^2 u$$

$$\frac{\partial v}{\partial t} = \Delta v + u^2 v$$

or, for a "steady state"

(3)
$$\Delta u + v^2 u = E_1 u$$

$$\Delta v + u^2 v = E_2 v$$

In <u>one</u> dimension a solution of the system (3) above with $u = v$ is

(4)
$$u = \frac{\sqrt{2}}{2} \frac{e^{-|x|/4}}{1 + e^{-|x|/2}}$$

if one requires the function to be square integrable and positive. For the case where one requires the function to be defined on a finite interval only—or, say, vanishing at two points on the line— one obtains elliptic functions.

The equation above is non-linear; in fact, in the way we have written it, it is a cubic in the unknown function. It seems to bear a formal similarity to the equations devised by Heisenberg. These are written as follows:

(5)
$$\gamma_\nu \frac{\partial}{\partial x_\nu} \psi \pm 1^2 \gamma_\mu \gamma_5 \psi (\psi^+ \gamma_\mu \gamma_5 \psi) = 0$$

It is a single equation (instead of a system of several linked ones) and the unknown function is defined not for scalar entities but for hyper-complex entities. To my knowledge there is no known exact solution for these but, using the Tamm-Dankoff method, Heisenberg claims to have found approximate solutions which seem to give constants resembling ratios of masses for some mesons.

A fuller treatment of a model given above of our linked equations would be

(6) $\quad \dfrac{\partial u_i}{\partial t} = \Delta u_i + \sum_{j,k}(a^i_{jk}u_ju_k)u_i \qquad i,j,k = 1\ldots n.$

The various coefficients now determine the various algebraic relations between the distributions whose mutual interactions and coexistence define the "elementary" objects.

The equations may be looked upon as generalizing, as a <u>partial</u> differential equation the equations of Volterra (<u>total</u> differential equations) on the coexistence of biological species.

The numerical work, undertaken to get at least an approximate idea of what the solutions of our system might be like, gave the following results and equations:

In <u>one</u> dimension, starting with a variety of initial u(x), v(x) at time t = 0 and integrating (2) one obtains very rapid convergence of u(x,t) and v(x,t) to the form given in (4), for example:

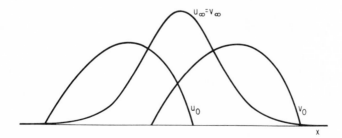

The solution (4) seems to be a strongly attracting fixed point in function space, at least in starting with positive u_0 and v. However, for certain pairs of non-positive initial u_0, v_0 there is convergence to a pair u_∞, v_∞ where u_∞ is the function given by (4) and $v_\infty = -u_\infty$.

In three dimensions, the story seems very involved; apparently the solution is not so strongly attractive.

It should be pointed out that if one requires in (3) the solution to have integral of its square equal to 1 then E_1 and E_2 can not be arbitrary, but, for positive u,v have to be $E_1 = E_2 = \dfrac{1}{16}$.

The numerical work in three dimensions is proceeding. There seems to be some evidence pointing to the possibility of several topologically distinct pairs of solutions.

The constants E_1 and E_2 can be interpreted as being "rest masses" of the system. That is because, in natural units, in the equations (6) and indeed in (3) they have dimensions of length l, (not length square as in Heisenberg (5)).

Given a length 1 one can use, as a first approximation, $m = \hbar/lc$ to obtain the "spectrum" of m.

Starting in (2) with two functions u_0 and v_0 of the form shown by

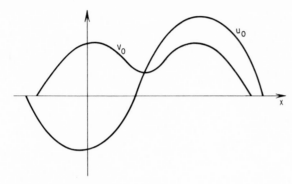

one obtains convergence to:

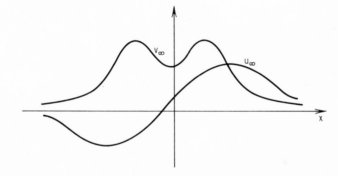

The Problem
of the Gas
of Hard Spheres

GEORGE E. UHLENBECK
The Rockefeller Institute
New York, N. Y.

ABSTRACT

The problem is whether a gas of which the molecules are hard spheres will show a phase transition as conjectured by Kirkwood in 1941. The mathematical formulation of this "model" problem was discussed and the various arguments (melting curve of Helium, numerical calculations by Alder and co-workers) which seem to indicate the existence of the Kirkwood transition were reviewed. However no rigorous proof exists. The importance of the problem as a general model for the solid-fluid phase transition was emphasized.

(Copyright © 1963 by Prentice-Hall, Inc.)

Phenomena Associated with the Oscillations of a Nonlinear Model String

The Problem of Fermi, Pasta, and Ulam

NORMAN J. ZABUSKY
Bell Telephone Laboratories, Inc.
Whippany, N. J.

ABSTRACT

To study the ergodic behavior of nonlinear, conservative and time-invariant systems, E. Fermi, J. R. Pasta, and S. Ulam (1955) considered a one-dimensional chain of N equimass particles coupled by nonlinear springs. The use of a numerical computing machine required that they discretize temporal operations, and so they were led to solving difference-difference equations. One case that has been extensively treated is given by the equation

(1) $\qquad [(\Delta t)^{-2}]\delta_j^2 y_i^j = [1 + \alpha(y_{i+1}^j - y_{i-1}^j)]\delta_i^2 y_i^j,$

where: i and j correspond to the spatial and temporal indices, respectively; and δ^2 is the central second-difference operator. The

(Copyright © 1963 by Prentice-Hall, Inc.)

"lowest-continuum" limit of this equation is the partial differential equation

(2) $y_{tt} = [1 + \varepsilon y_x] y_{xx}$, $(\varepsilon = 2\alpha/N)$,

which has at times been used as a model for the thermal conductivity of nonconducting crystals. It is shown that the exact solution of (2), treated as an initial-condition problem, is valid for all x for times $t < t_B = 0$ $(1/\varepsilon)$. At $t = t_B$, y_{xx} becomes singular. Up until this time the analytical solutions of (2) agree with the numerical solutions of (1). This is exhibited in several figures where a comparison of modal-energy vs. time is given.

The numerical solutions exhibit long-time periodicities, that is, no approach to a state of equipartition of energy. During one "recurrence" interval one finds that the location of the modal-energy maxima divides the interval in accordance with a Farey sequence. The concept of mode feeding is also evident in these results. In conclusion, a suggestion is made which may avoid the breakdown of the lowest continuum model and may duplicate the recurrence period observed in the numerical computations.

1. INTRODUCTORY REMARKS

This paper was motivated, as the subtitle implies, by the report by E. Fermi, J. Pasta, and S. Ulam[1] (FPU), published at Los Alamos in 1955. Since then, Ulam has reported the results of this com-

[1] E. Fermi, J. R. Pasta, and S. Ulam, "Studies of Nonlinear Problems I." Los Alamos Report No. LA-1940, May, 1955 (unpublished).

putational study at several meetings and conferences,[2] and has given

a qualitative and suggestive account of the phenomena in his "prob-

lem" book.[3] The present paper will emphasize the quantitative as-

pects of the numerical computations and will present new analytical

approaches to the general problem of nonlinear oscillations.

In the 1955 work, the authors addressed themselves to the study

of the ergodic behavior of nonlinear, conservative, and time-invar-

iant systems. If one imagines, as they did, a "continuous string"

with a small nonlinear interaction force, one has a mechanism for

coupling the initial energy among all the modes of oscillation or

stationary states of the corresponding linear system. The corre-

sponding system is the one obtained by setting the smallness pa-

rameter, α, associated with the nonlinearity, equal to zero. The fun-

damental period, t_{L1}, of the corresponding linear system is called

a "corresponding linear period" and is abbreviated as LP.

To study the problem, the authors employed the MANIAC com-

puter, and the continuous system was quantized (or discretized) in

both space and time, and was represented by a nonlinear difference-

difference equation. There is a fundamental disparity between the

continuous and discrete representations of nonlinear, physical sys-

[2](a) "Lectures on the Physics of Ionized Gases," Part IB, (T-706). Los Alamos Report No. LA-2055, October, 1956 (unpublished). (b) Proceedings of the Fourth Berkeley Symposium on Mathematical Statistics, (1960). Vol. III, Page 315 (University of California Press, 1961). (c) A lecture at a symposium held at the University of Maryland in April, 1961 (private communication).

[3]S. Ulam, A Collection of Mathematical Problems (Interscience Publishers, Inc., New York, 1960). Chapter 7, paragraph 8.

tems, and several of the comments made below will illuminate this difference.

Fermi, Pasta, and Ulam expected to observe an eventual energy sharing, or "equipartition" of energy, among the various degrees of freedom (normal modes), and they intended to calculate a relaxation time for the approach to this equilibrium configuration. In fact, however, they observed a completely different phenomenon. The system invariably reachieved the identical state from which it started after a large number of equivalent linear oscillations, this "recurrence" time being smaller than the Poincaré cycle[1] for the system. We designate this time interval as a "recurrence period," and will refer to it several times during the course of this paper.

It is the author's contention that the basic phenomena observed in the numerical computations have not as yet been explained analytically. Recently, however, M. D. Kruskal and the author have obtained analytical results that agree with the numerical computations for a time duration small compared to a recurrence period.

2. PRESENTATION OF THE DISCRETE MODEL

A one-dimensional chain of N-1 moving particles, each of mass m, served as the discrete model for the string. These mass particles, or beads, were coupled to their nearest neighbors by two types of nonlinear springs. In the first, the total restoring force of a spring was proportional to the sum of the extension plus the extension raised to an integral power ("analytic nonlinearity"), whereas in the second, the total restoring force was represented by a multisloped function of the extension ("broken nonlinearity").

The difference-difference equation solved by the computing machine was

$$(2.1) \qquad \frac{m}{k^2} \delta_j^2 y_i^j = \frac{1}{h} \{F_{i+(1/2)}^j - F_{i-(1/2)}^j\}, \qquad (i = 1, 2, \ldots, N-1)$$

where: m is the mass of a bead; k and h are the discreteness intervals in time and space, respectively; and δ^2 is the central second difference operator. For example, the temporal and spatial difference operators are given by

$$(2.2) \qquad \begin{aligned} \delta_j^2 y_i^j &= y_i^{j+1} - 2y_i^j + y_i^{j-1} \\ \delta_i^2 y_i^j &= y_{i+1}^j - 2y_i^j + y_{i-1}^j. \end{aligned}$$

The right side of (2.1) corresponds to the difference between nearest neighbor forces. For the nonlinear, "analytic" springs

$$(2.3) \qquad F_{i+(1/2)} = \kappa \left(\frac{y_{i+1} - y_i}{h} \right) + \kappa \alpha' \left(\frac{y_{i+1} - y_i}{h} \right)^{p+1},$$

and (2.1) becomes

$$(2.4) \qquad \begin{aligned} &(m/k^2) \delta_j^2 y_i^j \\ &= (\kappa/h^2) \{\delta_i^2 y_i + (\alpha'/h^p)[(y_{i+1} - y_i)^{p+1} - (y_i - y_{i-1})^{p+1}]\}. \end{aligned}$$

We have suppressed the (temporal) superscript j in (2.3) and the right side of (2.4), since it is clear that these displacements are evaluated at the same j. The broken nonlinearity is described by the force law:

$$F_{i+(1/2)} = \kappa(y_{i+1} - y_i), \quad \text{for } |y_{i+1} - y_i| \leq \Delta,$$

or

$$F_{i+(1/2)} = \Delta(\kappa - \kappa') + \kappa'(y_{i+1} - y_i), \quad \text{for } |y_{i+1} - y_i| \geq \Delta.$$

Thus, when the extension exceeds a preset value $(=\Delta)$, the linear spring constant jumps from one value (κ) to another value (κ'). Computationally, the above operations are treated more rapidly than those required for the analytic nonlinearities. This follows because only comparison operations are required (e.g., is $|y_{i+1} - y_i| \gtrless \Delta$?) to determine the coefficients A_1, A_{-1}, and A_0 of the model equation

$$(m/k^2)\,\delta_j^2 y_i^j = A_1(y_{i+1} - y_i) + A_{-1}(y_i - y_{i-1}) + A_0,$$

which replaces (2.4).

For the purposes of computation, FPU normalized (2.4) by choosing

(2.5) $m/\kappa = 1, \quad \alpha' = \alpha h^p,$

and

(2.6) $k = h(\Delta t),$

where (Δt) was taken smaller than 1 (e.g., $1/\sqrt{8}$), to satisfy the Courant-Friedrichs-Lewy condition[4] of the corresponding linear $(\alpha = 0)$ problem.

Remark. This is a necessary condition (since round-off errors exist) for the convergence of the solution of the linear difference-difference equation

$$(1/k^2)\,\delta_j^2 y_i^j = (c^2/h^2)\,\delta_i^2 y_i^j$$

[4]R. Courant, K. O. Friedrichs, and H. Lewy, Math. Annalen, **100**, 32, 1928.

to the solution of the corresponding linear partial differential equation, $y_{tt} = c^2 y_{xx}$. The condition requires that the "discretization velocity" imposed by the grid spacing, $h/k = 1/(\Delta t)$, be greater than the wave velocity c, or $h/k = 1/(\Delta t) > c$. If in (2.4) $\alpha = 0$ and $m/\kappa = 1$, the necessary condition is $(\Delta t) < 1$. The conditions and limitations associated with quasi-linear partial differential equations (essentially, the problem at hand) are more complicated. See, for example, G. E. Forsythe and W. R. Wasow, Finite-Difference Methods for Partial Differential Equations (John Wiley & Sons, Inc., New York, 1960), Sections 7 and 8.

It is interesting to observe that, if we are studying the problem of nonlinear coupled harmonic oscillators, then the discretization of second-time derivatives is the only approximation, and the size of (Δt) is determined by another consideration. For such a problem, the number of computation steps in the fundamental mode is given by

$$\eta_{c,1} = \frac{2.0(m/\kappa)^{1/2} N}{\Delta t}$$

and the number in the highest mode by

$$\eta_{c,N-1} \approx \frac{2.0(m/\kappa)^{1/2}}{\Delta t} \; .$$

If $(m/\kappa) = 1.0$, then (Δt) should be chosen much smaller than 1 (say $(\Delta t) \le 0.10$), so that we make a good approximation to the waveform of the highest mode. Computational effects related to the size of (Δt) have been observed by the author. One such effect is noted in the table following equation (4.2).

The initial conditions correspond to a standing-wave problem, that is, finite displacement (usually a pure mode) and zero rate of displacement,

(2.7) $y_i^0 = a \sin (i\pi/N)$ and $\left.\partial_t y_i\right|_{t=0} = 0.$

The boundary conditions ($i = 0, N$) correspond to fixed beads, $y_0 = y_N = 0.$

We will concentrate on the "quadratic" ($p = 1$) nonlinearity, because there is much more numerical data available for it, and primarily because the "lowest" continuum limit of this problem allows an exact analytical solution. Setting $p = 1$ and using (2.5) and (2.6), we can write (2.4) in the factored form,

(2.8) $[1/(\Delta t)^2]\delta_j^2 y_i^j = \delta_i^2 y_i^j [1 + \alpha(y_{i+1}^j - y_{i-1}^j)].$

Obviously, α measures the strength of the nonlinearity in the quantized model.

Equations (2.4) and (2.8) are also one-dimensional models for studying the thermal conductivity of non-conducting crystals.[5] The discretization of the temporal operations is a numerical approximation, while the spatial discretization is due to the atomic nature of the crystal lattice.

3. OBSERVED PHENOMENA

The energy variation of the first four modes given in Figure 1 of the original FPU report is reproduced, after scale normalizations,

[5]R. E. Peierls, Quantum Theory of Solids, (Clarendon Press, Oxford, 1955). Sections 2.2 and 2.4 treat the effect on thermal conductivity and thermal expansion of the anharmonic (that is, nonlinear) terms in the Hamiltonian.

in Figure 1. The conditions of the computation were $N = 32$, $\alpha = \frac{1}{4}$, $p = 1$, $\Delta t = 1/\sqrt{8}$, and the amplitude of (2.7), $a = 1$. The "modal" quantities, viz., amplitude, energy, etc., were obtained from a spatial decomposition of the waveform into normal modes. This is explained in detail in Section 5.

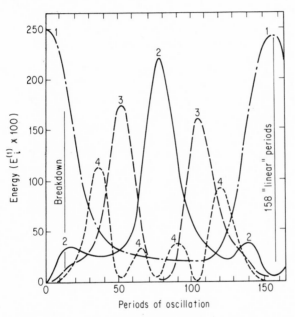

Figure 1. The energy (arbitrary units) in the low modes of the nonlinear string

$$(1/\Delta t)^2 \delta^2 y_i^j = [1 + \alpha(y_{i+1}^j - y_{i-1}^j)]\delta_i^2 y_i^j.$$

Reproduced from Fermi, Pasta, and Ulam,[1] Fig. 1.

We should note several phenomena:

(1) Initially all the energy is in the first mode, and after a recurrence period (158 linear periods) the identical initial state is almost obtained.

(2) The locations of the second and third modal maxima divide the recurrence interval into two and three equal parts, respectively.

(3) An "initial" maximum in the second mode is characteristic of the p = 1 numerical computations. The time-to-maximum (near the vertical line designated "breakdown") marks the end of the interval over which the analytic solutions obtained by M. D. Kruskal and the author are valid.

In Figure 2 we have the same conditions as those of Figure 1, except here N = 64 (a less granular string with the same nonlinear coupling).[6] For clarity, we have normalized the horizontal scale to read 1 after a recurrence period (corresponding to $T_{R1}/t_{L1} = 590$ LP). We have also removed the temporal variation of the modal energies and indicated only the locations of their maxima. We observe:

(1) More modes are excited and much more strongly. The second one mode has an initial maximum of the same amplitude as in Figure 1. This is as it should be if the analytical results are to be meaningful.

(2) The locations of the modal maxima for all modes up to and including mode n divide the recurrence interval in accordance with a Farey sequence.[7] The value n is 7 in Figure 2. The division is evident, in the projection of the modal maxima given at the bottom of Figure 2, where we see, for example, that each prime numbered

[6]Figure 2 is based on numerical computations made in 1961 by James L. Tuck of the Los Alamos Scientific Laboratories. The author gratefully acknowledges Tuck's generosity in making this data available to him.

[7]This observation was made by F. J. Dyson during the course of the author's talk. Theorems and properties associated with this sequence are given in G. H. Hardy and E. M. Wright, Introduction to the Theory of Numbers (Clarendon Press, Oxford, 1960).

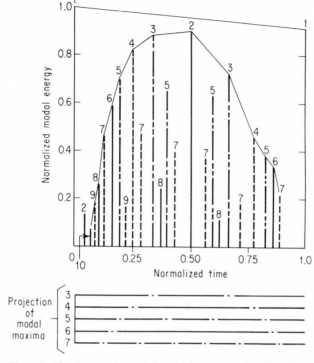

Figure 2. The time spectrum of the modal energy maxima (N = 64, $\alpha = \frac{1}{4}$, a = 1, and $\Delta t = 1/\sqrt{8}$).

mode divides the total recurrence interval in accordance with its number.

(3) The sequential occurrence of the modal maxima emphasizes the concept of mode feeding. Between a 3 and a 4 we find a 7; 5 and 3, 8; 2 and 3, 5; etc.

In 1961 J. L. Tuck of Los Alamos continued the computations for an N = 16 string for very long times and observed a "grand recurrence period." The basic pattern shown in Figures 1 and 2 repeats with more energy flowing into the higher modes and the peak energy

in the first mode decreasing monotonically. After several recurrence periods (7 in his case) the peak first-mode energy (which is
at .77 of its initial value) is a minimum, and the trend reverses.
After 14 recurrence periods, it achieves a value of .994 of its initial energy, and the trend again turns downward. Tuck has indicated
that he will soon publish the details of this and other computations.

The cubic, p = 2, nonlinearity also exhibited a recurrence, but
the modal spectrum was very different (no even modes exist). Not
all computations exhibited this "complete" recurrence. Figure 7
of the FPU report gives the energy spectrum for an N = 16 broken
nonlinear string with $\kappa' = 1.5\kappa$ (see p. 103). Also plotted is the
"remainder energy," which the author assumes is the sum of energies in modes 10 to 15. This remainder energy increases steadily
to 19% of the total initial energy at one-half of a recurrence period,
and to 43% of the initial energy at three-quarters of the recurrence
period (all that is plotted).

4. ANALYTICAL CONSIDERATIONS

A. Preliminaries

The open literature contains but one paper which attempts to
treat the FPU problem. In this paper,[8] Joseph Ford applied a modified Kryloff-Bogoliuboff procedure to study the nonlinear interaction of normal modes for the p = 1 problem (Eq. 2.8). This procedure assumed that the amplitude of the modal oscillations did not

---

[8]Joseph Ford, "Equipartition of Energy for Nonlinear Systems," J. Math. Phys. **2**, 787,
1961.

change—that is, Ford's equations "... retain the capacity for frequency modulation while discarding the mechanism for amplitude modulation."

These severe analytical restrictions are undoubtedly the explanation for the difference between his results and those presented by FPU. First, the location in time of the maxima and minima of Ford's modal energies are out of "phase" with those of FPU. For example, in his Figure 1 the third mode has maxima at $\frac{1}{6}$, $\frac{1}{2}$, and $\frac{5}{6}$ and minima at $\frac{1}{3}$ and $\frac{2}{3}$ of a recurrence interval. The FPU calculation shows a third-mode maxima at $\frac{1}{3}$ and $\frac{2}{3}$ and a minimum at $\frac{1}{2}$ of a recurrence interval. As observed above, the division of the recurrence interval in the manner described is a profound effect. A second difference between Ford and FPU is found in the magnitude and parameter dependence of the recurrence period, T_R. Ford calculates that the recurrence interval is due only to the "beating" of the first two linear modes. Thus,

$$(4.1) \qquad (T_R/t_{L1}) = \omega_1/(2\omega_1 - \omega_2) \approx (2N/\pi)^2 = 414(N/32)^2,$$

where t_{L1} is the linear period of the first mode. Using computational data from five different runs, the following phenomenological formula was computed:

$$(4.2) \qquad (T_R/t_{L1}) = 141\left[(N/32)^{1.38}/(4\alpha)^{0.5}\right] = 1.42(N^{1.38}/\alpha^{0.5}).$$

Two runs were made for fixed $N = 32$ and $\alpha = \frac{1}{4}$ and $\alpha = 1$. Three runs were made for fixed $\alpha = \frac{1}{4}$ and $N = 16$, 32, and 64. The latter runs are summarized in the following table:

Data for the Phenomenological Recurrence Relation

N	Source	$\dfrac{t_{L1}^*}{N}$	$\dfrac{T_R}{t_{L1}}$ (numerical)	$\dfrac{T_R}{t_{L1}}$ (Eq. 4.2)	% Error
16	LASL	16	51.6	53.9	−4.5
32	LASL	20	145	141	+2.8
64	BTL**	20	341	354	−3.7

LASL = Los Alamos Scientific Laboratory
BTL = Bell Telephone Laboratories, Inc.
*$(t_{L1}/N) \doteq \eta_{c,N-1}$ number of computation steps in the period corresponding to the highest mode, ω_{N-1}.
**The conditions for this run are the same as for the run described by Figure 2, except that here $\Delta t = 0.01$, whereas for Figure 2 $\Delta t = 1/\sqrt{8}$. This indicates that the size of Δt affects t_R.

Aside from differing by a factor of three, (4.2) shows a different N dependence as well as an explicit α dependence. At present the data is crude, and the author feels that in (4.2) the exponent on N may actually be closer to 1.5 than to 1.38.

B. Continuum Limit[9]

One can obtain an equivalent continuum representation for these problems by assuming that spatial and temporal differences can be expanded in terms of a Taylor series. For example,

$$(4.3) \quad y_{i\pm1} - y_i = [\pm h\, \partial_x y + (h^2/2)\partial_x^2 y \pm (h^3/3!)\partial_x^3 y + \ldots]_{x=i}$$

$$(4.4) \quad y^{j\pm i} - y^j = [\pm k\, \partial_t y + (k^2/2)\partial_t^2 y \pm (k^3/3!)\partial_t^3 y - \ldots]_{t=j}$$

Making these substitutions in (2.8), we obtain

$$\partial_t^2 y - [1 + \varepsilon(\partial_x y)]\partial_x^2 y = \left(\frac{h}{12}\right)^2 \{[1 + \varepsilon(\partial_x y)]\partial_x^4 y + 2\partial_x^2 y\, \partial_x^3 y$$
$$(4.5)$$
$$- (k^2/h^2)\partial_t^4 y\} + O(h^4) + O(k^4)$$

where

$$(4.6) \quad \varepsilon = 2\alpha h = 2\alpha/N.$$

[9]The idea of treating this general problem in its continuum limit was suggested to the author by M. D. Kruskal. Several aspects of the work reported here were either discussed with or carried out in conjunction with M. D. Kruskal.

Equation (4.6) follows if we normalize the discrete string of length N to a continuous string of length one. The right side of (4.5) contains an infinite number of terms, each involving higher order space or time derivatives. We obtain the lowest continuum limit by assuming that all terms $0(h^2) = 0(1/N^2)$ and $0(k^2)$ are negligible. Thus

(4.7) $y_{tt} - (1 + \varepsilon y_x)^{2\gamma} y_{xx} = 0,$

where we have added the exponent 2γ to the term which multiplies the second space derivative, since it does not complicate the mathematical procedures which follow. We have introduced the subscript notation for partial differentiation, for example, $y_t = \partial_t y$. It will be used throughout, except in ambiguous situations. In the definition of ε in (4.6) we have assumed that the strength of the nonlinearity, α, increases with N, such that ε is a finite but small number.

Equation (4.7) is also the Lagrangian representation for describing longitudinal wave propagation in a nonlinear, hysteresis-free, solid continuum. $y = y(x,t)$ is the displacement of an element of the solid from an initial reference position, and

(4.8) $F^2 = (1 + \varepsilon y_x)^{2\gamma}$

is related to the derivative of the stress with respect to the strain. The Lagrangian density for the system (4.7) is

(4.9) $\mathcal{L} = \dfrac{1}{2} y_t^2 - \dfrac{(1 + \varepsilon y_x)^{2\gamma+2}}{\varepsilon^2 (2\gamma + 2)(2\gamma + 1)} + (1 + y_x)$

or

(4.10) $\mathcal{L} = \dfrac{1}{2} (y_t^2 - y_x^2) - \varepsilon (2\gamma/3!) y_x^3 - 0 (\varepsilon^2 y_x^4).$

If $2\gamma = 1$, then the series expansion given in (4.10) terminates, such that terms $0(\varepsilon^2 y_x^4) = 0$.

The analytical methods to be described are applicable to the more general case where F^2 can be written as the product of an arbitrary function of y_x and an arbitrary function of y_t. Thus, numerous physical wave problems can be treated, including those from hydrodynamics, plasmas, solids, and electrodynamics. In fact, Ornstein and Zernike[10] attempted to explain the thermal conductivity of nonconducting crystals by using (4.7) with 2γ taken as unity. They linearized the equation early in the analysis and did not obtain the most interesting results.

C. An Exact Solution for the Continuum-Limit Equation

The author has succeeded in obtaining an exact solution for (4.7) subject to the appropriate continuum initial conditions.[11] The material given here is for the most part a digest (employing a more compact notation than that given in the above paper). The boundary conditions

$$y(0, t) = y(1, t) = 0$$

were replaced by an equivalent set of conditions, namely: oddness, $y(-x, t) = -y(x, t)$; and periodicity, $y(x = 2, t) = y(x, t)$. Thus, we dealt with an initial condition problem.

The equation was cast into an equivalent linear representation

[10]L. S. Ornstein and F. Zernike, "Contributions to the Kinetic Theory of Solids II. The Unimpeded Spreading of Heat Even in the Case of Deviations from Hooke's Law," Proc. Nederlansche Akad. van wetens (Proc. Royal Acad. Sci., Amsterdam) 19, 1295, 1917. Their equation 1 is (4.7) with $2\gamma = 1$.

[11]N. J. Zabusky, "Exact Solution for the Vibrations of a Nonlinear Continuous Model String," J. Math. Phys. 3, 1028, 1962.

by means of the hodograph transformation. It was shown that the solution of this equation is not defined for all times $t \geq 0$. At $t = t_B$ the second space derivative, y_{xx}, develops a singularity. This "breakdown" of the analytic solution is manifest in the vanishing of a Jacobian. The presence of breakdown is an important concept, as will be seen when we compare the analytic solutions with the computer solutions.

To obtain the exact solution, one rewrites (4.7) as two coupled partial differential equations by introducing the auxiliary variables

(4.11) $u = y_x$ and $v = y_t$.

The consistency of this definition requires

(4.12) $u_t - v_x = 0$,

and (4.7) becomes

(4.13) $v_t - (1 + \varepsilon u)^{2\gamma} u_x = 0$.

If we multiply (4.12) by $F = (1 + \varepsilon u)^{\gamma}$ and add and subtract the result to (4.13), we obtain the pair of characteristic equations

(4.14) $r_t - F r_x$ and $s_t + F s_x = 0$,

where the Riemann invariants r and s are given by

(4.15) $\begin{matrix} r \\ s \end{matrix} = \pm \frac{1}{2}v + \frac{1}{2} \int^u F(u')\,du' = \pm \frac{1}{2}v + \frac{(1 + \varepsilon u)^{1+\gamma}}{2\varepsilon(1 + \gamma)}$.

A hodograph[12] or inversion transformation will linearize (4.14), for F is explicitly a function of u [and therefore $(r + s)$]. If we take

(4.16) $\begin{matrix} r_x = jt_s, & s_x = -jt_r, \\ r_t = -jx_s, & s_t = jx_r, \end{matrix}$

---

[12]R. Courant and K. O. Friedrichs, Supersonic Flow and Shock Waves (Interscience Publishers, Inc., New York, 1948). See section 30, p. 62 and section 103, p. 248.

where the Jacobian

(4.17) $j = r_x s_t - s_x r_t = -2F r_x s_x,$

then the equations (4.14) become

(4.18) $x_r - Ft_r = 0$ and $x_s + Ft_s = 0.$

If we eliminate x from this pair of equations, we obtain

(4.19) $t_{rs} + (2F)^{-1}[F_s t_r + F_r t_s] = t_{rs} + [n/(r + s)][t_r + t_s] = 0,$

where

(4.20) $n = \dfrac{\frac{1}{2}\gamma}{\gamma + 1} = \dfrac{1}{6}$ for $2\gamma = 1.$

The second equation of (4.19) is the Euler-Poisson-Darboux equation and follows because

(4.21) $F = (1 + \varepsilon u)^\gamma = [\varepsilon(1 + \gamma)(r + s)]^{\gamma/(1+\gamma)}.$

The x equation, obtained by eliminating t from (4.18), is identical to (4.19), except that n is replaced by $-n$.

The nature of the quadratic nonlinearity permitted us to write F and the coefficient of $[t_r + t_s]$ in (4.19) as closed form expressions involving $r + s$. The lowest continuum limit of the equation describing the cubic nonlinearity does not allow this closed form representation. The equation for this case is obtained from (2.4) with $p = 2$, as

(4.22) $y_{tt} = [1 + \varepsilon^2 y_x^2]^{2\gamma} y_{xx}$

where we have added the exponent 2γ to the bracketed expression and where

(4.23) $\varepsilon^2 = 3\alpha/N^2.$

The appropriate Riemann invariants are derived from the definition, given in (4.15) as

(4.24) $\quad \begin{smallmatrix} r \\ s \end{smallmatrix} = \pm\frac{1}{2}v + \frac{1}{4}\{u(1 + \varepsilon^2u^2)^{1/2} + \varepsilon^{-1}\log[\varepsilon u + (1 + \varepsilon^2u^2)^{1/2}]\},$

where we have set $2\gamma = 1$. Using (4.24), one cannot obtain a closed form expression for u or F in terms of $(r + s)$. On the other hand, if we consider the model where $2\gamma = -1$ in (4.22), we can obtain a closed form representation. The linear partial differential equation in t is

(4.25) $\quad t_{rs} - \frac{1}{2}\varepsilon[\tanh \varepsilon(r + s)][t_r + t_s] = 0,$

and the appropriate Riemann invariants are

(4.26) $\quad \begin{smallmatrix} r \\ s \end{smallmatrix} = \frac{1}{2}[\pm v + \varepsilon^{-1}\sinh^{-1}\varepsilon u].$

To the author's knowledge, equation (4.25) has not been treated in the literature.

If one applies Riemann's method of integration[13] to (4.19), one can express the solution for $t(\xi,\eta)$ as an integral of the Riemann function (a function characteristic of the t differential equation) weighted by the appropriate initial condition. So ξ and η are the r and s coordinates of a point at which the solution is desired. The Riemann function [the solution of the homogeneous equation adjoint to (4.19)] is expressible in terms of Legendre functions when n is not an integer (our case) and in terms of rational fractions when n is an integer. Similar considerations[14] yield the solution $x(\xi,\eta)$ as

[13]A. Sommerfeld, Partial Differential Equations in Physics (Academic Press Inc., New York, 1949). See Chap. 3, paragraph 11.

[14]See Zabusky, op. cit., Sec. 5C.

the sum of an integral taken over the initial-condition interval plus non-integrated terms associated with the end points of the interval.

The breakdown of the analytic solution is rigorously established if one can show that t_r vanishes at some point in the inverse (r,s) plane. This follows from the definition of j in (4.17) and t_r in (4.18), namely,

(4.27) $t_r = F^{-1}x_r = (jF)^{-1}s_t = [2r_xF]^{-1}$,

or

(4.28) $t_r = (2r_x)^{-1}[\varepsilon(1 + \gamma)(r + s)]^{-\gamma/(1+\gamma)}$,

since

$$j = -2Fr_xs_x.$$

Thus, if t_r vanishes, then $r_x \propto y_{xx} \to \infty$, since $(r + s)$ always remains finite.

One can show[15] that the time-to-breakdown, t_{B1}, is given as

(4.29) $t_{B1} = 4/\varepsilon a\pi^2$,

where the subscript 1 indicates a first-mode initial condition.

To formally prove that t_r vanishes, one must first "unfold" the inverse Riemann plane by using a technique developed by G. S. S. Ludford.[16] Because the initial conditions in the physical plane are periodic, the entire x axis from $-\infty$ to $+\infty$ is projected onto a line (the main diagonal) of finite length in the (r,s) plane, as shown in Figure 3. This follows from the definition of r and s given in

---

[15]See Zabusky, op. cit., Sec. 5D.

[16]G. S. S. Ludford, "On an Extension of Riemann's Method of Integration with Application to One-dimensional Gas Dynamics," Proc. Cambridge Phil. Soc. 48, 499, (1952) and, "Extensions in the Applicability of Riemann's Formula", J. Rational Mechanics 3, 77, (1954).

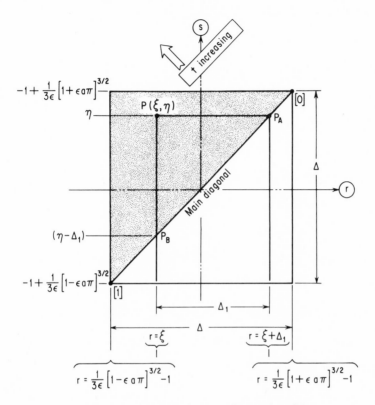

Figure 3. The (r, s) plane for a periodic initial condition.

(4.15) when v = 0 and $u|_{t=0}$ is a periodic function. Thus, the main diagonal and the triangular region above it are multi-valued. For times smaller than ($\frac{1}{4}$) of a LP, Riemann's integration method requires one to choose a contour within the triangle above the main diagonal. Solutions for increasing time are found by moving upward and to the left on the inverse Riemann plane. For times $> \frac{1}{4}$ (LP), one must unfold[17] the initial condition line, as shown in Figure 4. The essential requirement for unfolding is that r be invariant along

[17]See Zabusky, op. cit., Sec. 5A.

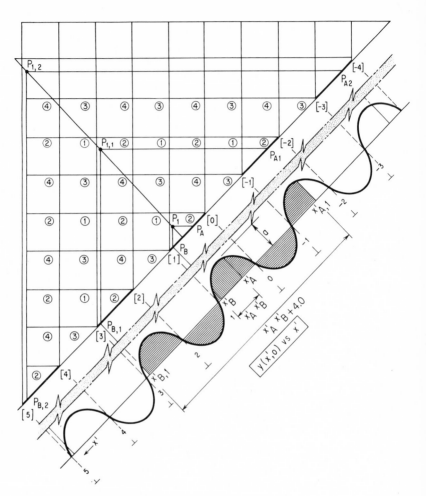

Figure 4. The unfolded (r, s) plane for a periodic initial condition.

a vertical characteristic and s be invariant along a horizontal characteristic. The sinusoidal curve below the shaded region corresponds to the initial condition in the physical plane. The elapsed time intervals that correspond to moving from $P_1 \rightarrow P_{1,1}$ and $P_{1,1} \rightarrow P_{1,2}$ are almost one fundamental LP. The region of the initial condition line in the physical plane which affects the solution at

$P_{1,1}$ is obtained by projecting along characteristics from $P_{1,1}$ to the main diagonal.

It can be shown that breakdown is associated with the intersection of neighboring characteristics that emanate from those points of the initial condition line where $y(x', 0)$ has maxima and minima (the midpoints of the intervals). Breakdown takes place along the $r \rightarrow (x + t)$ characteristics that emanate from minima regions and along the $s \rightarrow (x - t)$ characteristics that emanate from maxima regions. If one considers the breakdown region in detail, one can show[18] that $u = y_x$ goes from a single-valued to a three-valued function, or that r_x and $y_{xx}(x, t)$ become singular.

The exact solution, when expanded <u>uniformly</u> to $0(1)$, can be written as[19]

(4.30) $u = y_x = \frac{1}{2} a\pi C_+ + 0(\varepsilon)$

(4.31) $v = y_t = \frac{1}{2} a\pi C_- + 0(\varepsilon)$,

where

(4.32) $C_{\pm} = \cos \pi x_B \pm \cos \pi x_A$,

(4.33) $S_{\pm} = \sin \pi x_B \pm \sin \pi x_A$,

(4.34) $x_{A \atop B} = x \mp t \mp (T/\pi) \cos \pi \, x_{A \atop B} + 0(\varepsilon)$,

(4.35) $T = t/t_B = \frac{1}{4} \varepsilon a\pi^2 t$.

[18]M. D. Kruskal and N. J. Zabusky, work in progress. To be published as, "A Stroboscopic-Perturbation Procedure for Treating a Class of Nonlinear Wave Equations." This paper contains a general procedure and a specific application to the FPU problem. The application includes: (1) a derivation of the modal amplitude and phase from the waveform; and (2) a detailed study of the waveform in the breakdown region.

[19]See Zabusky, op. cit., Sec. 6. The results given in (6.8) and (6.9) (which correspond to (4.34) above) are correct only to $0(1)$. That is, we treat the solution over time intervals $0(1/\epsilon)$, and thus terms $0(\epsilon t) = 0(T) = 0(1)$. The correct uniform solution to $0(\epsilon)$ is given in the reference cited in footnote 18.

Thus, our solution for y_x or y_t is given as a function of x and t by the implicit relations, (4.34). The results, (4.30) thru (4.35), are obtained more directly by using a perturbation procedure developed by M. D. Kruskal and the author.[18]

5. COMPARISONS OF THE ANALYTICAL AND NUMERICAL COMPUTATIONS

A comparison between the analytical and numerical results is meaningful only during the time interval over which the former is valid—that is, up until $t = t_B$ or $T = 1$. This is a small elapsed time in comparison with the recurrence time. This is readily seen if one normalizes the phenomenological recurrence time, given in (4.2), with respect to the breakdown interval.

$$(5.1) \qquad \frac{T_R}{t_{B1}} = 10.9 \left(\frac{N}{32}\right)^{0.38} (4\alpha)^{0.5}$$

The results of the FPU calculations are presented in the form of modal energy vs. time. This form of presentation is adopted below, although it is an incomplete description of the waveform $y(x,t)$ because the modal phase information is lacking.

The total energy of the system is obtained by integrating the Hamiltonian density over a fixed spatial interval

$$(5.2) \qquad E_T = \tfrac{1}{2} \int_{-1}^{1} dx \left[y_t^2 + y_x^2 + (\varepsilon/3) y_x^3 \right],$$

and is a conserved quantity. For convenience in computation we omit terms $O(\varepsilon)$ in the Hamiltonian density. For the range of parameters being considered, this introduces an error of 1.6% in the total energy. Thus,

(5.3) $E_T^{(0)} = \frac{1}{2} \int_{-1}^{1} dx \{ [y_t^{(0)}]^2 + [y_x^{(0)}]^2 \},$

where the superscripts in parenthesis indicate that the argument is taken uniformly to zero order.

For a pure initial value problem, $y(x',0) = a \sin \pi x'$ and $y_t(x',0) = 0$, one finds that a spatial Fourier decomposition of $y_x^{(0)} = \frac{1}{2} a \pi C_+$ and $y_t^{(0)} = \frac{1}{2} a \pi C_-$ yields a cosine and sine series, respectively. Thus, if

(5.4) $A_n = \int_{-1}^{1} y_x^{(0)} \cos \pi nx\, dx,$ and $B_n = \int_{-1}^{1} y_t^{(0)} \sin \pi nx\, dx,$

then after some computation we find

(5.5) $\begin{bmatrix} A_n \\ B_n \end{bmatrix} = 2a\pi \left\{ \dfrac{J_n(nT)}{nT} \right\} \begin{bmatrix} \sin \frac{1}{2}\pi n & \cos \frac{1}{2}\pi n \\ \cos \frac{1}{2}\pi n & -\sin \frac{1}{2}\pi n \end{bmatrix} \begin{bmatrix} \cos \pi nt \\ \sin \pi nt \end{bmatrix},$

where matrix multiplication is understood. The zero-order energy is given by

(5.6) $E_T^{(0)} = \frac{1}{2} \sum_{n=1}^{\infty} (A_n^2 + B_n^2) = \sum_{n=1}^{\infty} E_n^{(0)},$

where

(5.7) $E_n^{(0)} = 2 [a\pi J_n(nT)/(nT)]^2 .$

The modal energy curves that (5.7) yield—the so-called "analytic" results—are plotted in Figures 5 through 7 with the normalized modal energy curves obtained from the numerical computations. The numerical results were obtained for $\alpha = \frac{1}{4}$ and $N = 16$, 32, and 64. From the definition of t_{B1}, one observed that the larger the N, the larger the number of linear periods of oscillation in a breakdown interval.

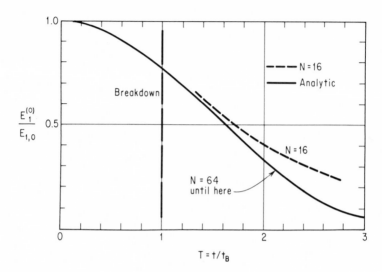

Figure 5. The first mode energies for the analytic and computational solutions.

Figure 5 is a comparison of the normalized first-mode energies. The analytic curve and N = 64 curve agree even beyond breakdown and up until the time shown. The more granular N = 16 curve begins to diverge immediately after the breakdown time. A comparison of the normalized second-mode energies is given in Figure 6, where the vertical scale is stretched by a factor of four. Up until the breakdown time the N = 32 and N = 64 curves agree with the analytic curve, whereas the N = 16 curve diverges from it slightly before breakdown. After breakdown we again see that the more granular strings diverge much more rapidly from the analytic curve. As a rule of thumb one can locate the equivalent breakdown time for these problems where the second-mode energy has its first maximum (the "initial maximum" mentioned previously). Since the am-

plitude of this maximum is calculable from the analytic solutions
(continuous model), it should be a quantity which is almost invariant
to the size of α or N, so long as the latter is sufficiently large, say
≥ 32. For the analytic solution, $\text{Max}\{E_2^{(0)}/E_{1,0}\} = .13$.

The good agreement between the large N numerical solutions
and the analytic solution after breakdown probably arises from one
or both of the following considerations. First, for a certain elapsed
time after breakdown, the larger N is, the smaller is the percentage of the total string length which is multi-valued. Second, the
waveform of the actual (numerical) string does not differ greatly
from the "averaged" analytic waveform which the Fourier decomposition implies.

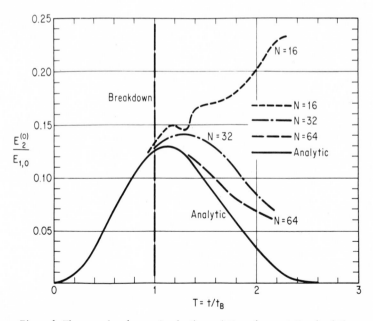

Figure 6. The second mode energies for the analytic and computational solutions.

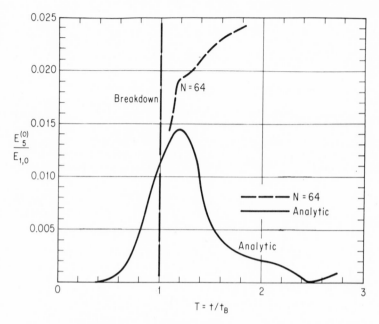

Figure 7. The fifth mode energies for the analytic and computational solutions.

In Figure 7 we compare the analytic and N = 64 fifth-mode energies. There is good agreement up until breakdown and rapid divergence thereafter. This is to be expected, since phenomena associated with higher mode numbers are more strongly affected by the continuum approximation. The significance of the breakdown time is also demonstrated by a graph of the numerical remainder energies vs. time. Two such curves are plotted on a semi-logarithmic scale in Figure 8 for the N = 64 string. Such a curve (the sum of modes 6-63) shows an exponential growth in the time interval before breakdown and a smooth leveling off at breakdown. For comparison, the energy in modes 2-5 has also been given.

6. CONCLUSIONS

The problem treated above has been considered from two points of view: first, as a nonlinear difference-difference equation whose solution has been obtained numerically for a selected set of initial conditions; second, as a second-order hyperbolic wave equation with corresponding initial conditions. The second can be considered as the lowest-order continuum limit of the first. As mathematical problems they are both interesting; as problems motivated by natural phenomena either or none may be meaningful.

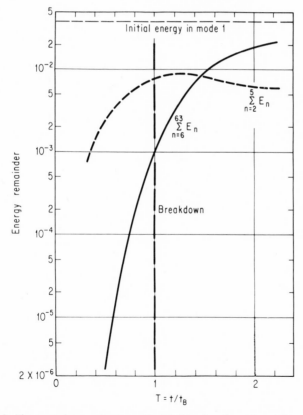

Figure 8. The remainder energies for an N = 64 string ($\alpha = \frac{1}{4}$, a = 1, and $\Delta t = 1/\sqrt{8}$).

The temporal variable is normally considered a continuous variable, and the appropriate operators to use are derivatives and integrals or their equivalent. Similarly, the spatial variable is meaningfully and successfully treated as a continuous variable in many physical problems. On the other hand, the atomic nature of a crystal lattice is one of many physical applications where spatial operations must be discretized This suggests a differential-difference equation as an appropriate description of the physical process.

We have proven that a continuous string exhibits a breakdown after a finite time interval. A beaded string (differential-difference equation) is a dispersive medium, and any mechanism which causes a flow of energy to the higher modes will eventually be modified. For example, either the dispersive mechanism alone is important after a finite time, or there is a competition between the original (in our case a nonlinear) mechanism and the dispersive mechanism.

The dispersiveness of the beaded string can be treated in a continuum representation by keeping all or some (hopefully, the latter) of the higher derivative terms that were omitted in taking the lowest-continuum limit [see eq. (4.5)]. In recent years, much effort has gone into resolving the singularities or breakdowns of hydrodynamic problems by incorporating "viscosity-like" higher derivative terms.[20] These viscosity terms are dissipative and not dis-

[20]P. D. Lax, "Hyperbolic Systems of Conservation Laws II," Communs. Pure and Appl. Math. 10, 537, 1957. In particular, see section 3. O. A. Oleinik, "Construction of a Generalized Solution of the Cauchy Problem of a Quasilinear Equation of First Order by the Introduction of Vanishing Viscosity." Uspehi Mat. Nauk. 14, No. 2 (86), 159, 1959.

persive in nature, and one would not expect the mathematical tech-

niques for treating the former to be applicable to the latter.

The proper term(s) to include involve those with the highest de-

rivatives and largest coefficients. Obviously, the leading term of

(4.5) satisfies these criteria and the equation which may describe

some of the long-time phenomena is,

(6.1) $y_{tt} - y_{xx}[1 + \varepsilon y_x] = (h^2/12) y_{xxxx}$, $(h = 1/N)$.

Three time scales are suggested by this equation. For a string

of length 1, the first two terms yield the period of oscillation of the

linear system, $t_{L1} = 2$. The first three terms have the breakdown

time inherent in them, $t_{B1} = 0(1/\varepsilon)$. Now the third time scale is

motivated as follows. We divide through by $(\varepsilon h^2/12)$. If, at points on

the string, $(y_x y_{xx})/(h^2/12)$ is of the same order of magnitude as

$(y_x 4)/\varepsilon$, then the competition between these two terms will affect

the new time scale, $\tau^2 = t^2(\varepsilon h^2/12)$. If $\tau = 0(1)$ when new phenom-

ena occur, the new time scale is

(6.2) $t_R = 0(\varepsilon^{-1/2} h^{-1}) = 0(N^{1.5}/\alpha^{0.5})$.

The resemblance of (6.2) to the phenomenological recurrence time,

(4.2), motivates the use of $(h^2/12) y_{xxxx}$ to resolve the discontinuity.

DISCUSSION

Ross: I would like to know if the peculiar periodicities have any-

thing to do with breakdown?

Zabusky: I believe not, although I have no verification.

Kruskal: What a breakdown says is that the theory which gives the stroboscopic picture can't be carried immediately past the breakdown point. One would hope that one could make a connection between the regions before and after breakdown. Maybe the breakdown is momentary, maybe it persists. If you use the difference equation there should be no breakdown. But then that messes up the stroboscopic picture which then is not periodic.

Dyson: Is there just one particular moment at which all these epsilons sum up, and that's presumably where the kink occurs? Then afterwards the waveform will be perfectly smooth again. I don't know whether these expansions according to your method are a series representation of the solution after breakdown.

Zabusky: No, they're not.

Dyson: If you take this business of the Bessel function seriously and put the Fourier series together, doesn't it still satisfy the partial differential equation after breakdown? Afterwards the wave forms will be perfectly smooth again. Is there any reason to believe that the Fourier representation would not be correct after the breakdown.

Kruskal: I think that one wouldn't expect it to be correct. Why should it be? You do not have the phase.

Dyson: Well, simply because the series will converge very uniformly. The lack of uniform convergence occurs where each of these Bessel functions is a maximum. You can see that it converges uniformly no matter what the phases are.

Kruskal: But you do not know the limit if you do not have the phases.

Dyson: The solution has to be a continuous and differentiable function. But still each term of the Fourier series is continuous, only the convergence is not uniform across the particular time. That seems to be the only thing that happens.

Grad: Not just at that time. The discontinuity will be present afterwards.

Friedrichs: Breakdown is in the total shape of the string and not for the modes:

Grad: But there is no simple equation for the modes.

Dyson: If you believe equation (5.5) it seems to me that the solution must persist.

Grad: But the partial differential equation isn't defined beyond that time, because the equation involves second derivatives and at some point in space one of these is singular after $t = t_B$. It's not a conservation type either. There's no theory for the equation. Think about whether there is a solution that this Fourier series approximates.

Kruskal: The problem is not defined after breakdown and the Fourier series representation has no meaning after this point.

Dyson: I would just take the equation (4.7) as it stands. Since this series converges uniformly it can be substituted into equation (4.7).

Grad: You have to compute a second derivative to put in this equation.

Dyson: But you can differentiate this series twice.

Kruskal: In any case once the singularity occurs you don't really know what is happening, and since you want to compare it with data such as the numerical calculations, you have to find a way to say what you meant. Now with the calculations you know what you meant because that is a discrete problem. This is one way of breaking the degeneracy, and this is what we're trying to do—by putting in the higher derivative terms which come from that difference equation. We keep granularity terms and hope to be able to carry through the singularity by a matching analysis in the neighborhood of the singularity. But we found great difficulty in seeing what was happening. We hope by comparing with some detailed numerical data that we can find an appropriate equation to use in the region after the singularity has formed. We would hope to explain the recurrence period in this manner.

Ulam: What would you say is the true differential equation for the string?

Zabusky: This differential equation is right until breakdown. It is just as in hydrodynamics, when a shock develops after a finite time interval. When the higher derivatives get very large near the breakdown time, you excite a "beam-type" phenomena, which I neglected here. The "bending" phenomena, enter as

$$(h^2/12) \cdot [(1 + \varepsilon \partial_x y) \cdot \partial_x^4 y + 2\partial_x^2 y \cdot \partial_x^3 y - (k^2/h^2) \partial_t^4 y] + 0(h^4) + 0(k^4).$$

By the way, it's interesting that the $\partial_x^4 y$ term is of opposite sign to that in the usual beam vibration equation. It is diffusion like rather than wave like and its solution, neglecting the nonlinearities, will not involve the Fresnel integrals.

Ulam: So if you keep higher derivative terms, maybe you'd be closer to the difference equation?

Zabusky: That's the idea that we have.

Kruskal: The fact you see, that the actual data disagree with the analysis when you go past the point, is due to granularity. This shows how important the granularity problem is in getting past the singularity. Up to the breakdown time they agree beautifully, but afterward they all go different ways. The granularity has apparently become important just for the singularity, but not until then.

Dyson: It's clear that the granularity is important when you have a singularity, obviously. But it is quite plausible from this continuation problem that it doesn't have trouble at that point. You may be misled by the granularity.

Kruskal: There are many differential equations that could have this as a finite difference equation.

Dyson: I'm just speaking of that differential equation.

Kruskal: That does not define the solution because of the breakdown.

Stochastic Approach to Cosmology*

JERZY NEYMAN
University of California
Berkeley, California

1. INTRODUCTION

The purpose of the present paper is to give a brief account of the work, mostly joint with Elizabeth L. Scott, done over the last decade or so [12]-[19]** on a stochastic model of what Edwin Hubble described as the "realm of the nebulae" [6]. Every step in a novel direction taken in a domain of study of long standing begins with the realization, justified or not, that in the earlier approaches there is something either wrong or inadequate. The nature of our work is easier to explain if we begin with its motivation, that is with the description of what appears to us to be an inadequacy in

---

*This paper was prepared with the partial support of the National Science Foundation Grant GP-10.

**Figures in brackets refer to the list of references at the end of this article.

(Copyright © 1963 by Prentice-Hall, Inc.)

the classical mathematical work on problems of cosmology.

The cosmologies that are here termed classical are those due to Einstein and to his followers. This work was initiated long before the era of large telescopes and, therefore, much before the beginning of the earnest detailed study of the various extragalactic objects. Little was known or discussed about the individual characteristics of these objects and, therefore, in attempts to treat the whole realm mathematically it appeared natural to ignore individuality. Also, at that time probability theory was in its infancy and the mathematical apparatus most usually applied to problems of physical science was that of deterministic differential equations. As a result of these two principal factors, the classical cosmologies are predominantly deterministic and the mathematical work about the realm of the galaxies is concerned not with galaxies but with "substratum," a kind of fluid, the properties of which at each point are supposed to coincide with reality only in averages taken over large volumes in space surrounding the given point.

While the above "smoothing" idealizations became firmly established in mathematical cosmological work, observational astronomy proceeded in the opposite direction. This is symbolized by Figures 1, 2 and 3. Figures 1 and 2 reproduce photographs of galaxies belonging to two different "morphological types," spiral and elliptical. Beginning with the pioneer work of Edwin Hubble in the 1930's, work on morphological types of galaxies has been developing rapidly in various directions, in particular by N. U. Mayall,

Figure 1. Triplet of spiral galaxies. (Photograph courtesy of
Professor Gérard de Vaucouleurs.)

W. W. Morgan [11] and Gérard de Vaucouleurs [23]. T. L. Page
found [21] that on the average the masses of elliptical galaxies ex-
ceed by far those of the spirals. All these and other similar studies
fall outside of the theory concerned with "smoothed-out substratum." Figure 3 represents another frequent subject of study by
observational astronomers, namely a cluster of galaxies. While in
the 1930's the opinion was prevalent that, by and large, galaxies
are distributed in space "with statistical uniformity," catalogues
of clusters of galaxies are now being published. The first is due to
G. O. Abell [1]. It was recently followed by an impressive first
volume of a many volume catalogue of galaxies and clusters com-

Figure 2. The large object in the center is an elliptical galaxy.
(Photograph courtesy of Professor Gérard de Vaucouleurs.)

piled by F. Zwicky and his co-workers [26]. Here again we have an example where the objects of preoccupation of observational astronomy are outside of the mathematical apparatus used in classical cosmology.

This contrast between the domain of current observations of individual galaxies and their clusters on the one hand, and the theory dealing with the smoothed-out substratum on the other, is the more striking because every effort to verify empirically the conclusions of the theory must deal with observations of objects whose very existence this theory ignores. Thus, in order to effect a verification it is necessary to adopt a number of ad hoc hypotheses and, as a result, the conclusions are open to question.

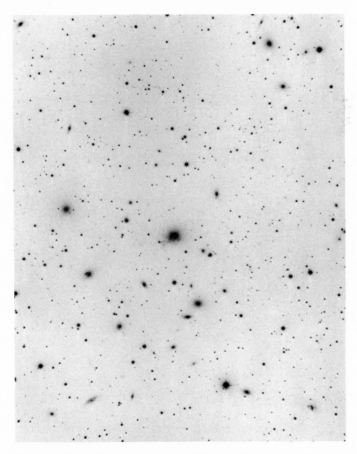

Figure 3. Reproduction of a photograph of Perseus Cluster of galaxies taken with the 200-inch Hale telescope of the Mt. Palomar Observatory. All objects with fuzzy edges are galaxies. The elongated images of galaxies are more easily identifiable. Round objects with sharp edges are stars. (Photograph courtesy of Professor Rudolph Minkowski.)

The above considerations are the basis of the work of Elizabeth L. Scott and myself. We believe that the mathematical tool appropriate for the treatment of problems of cosmology is the theory of stochastic processes, not that of deterministic differential equations. Thus, we set for ourselves the problem of devising a stochastic process embodying concepts that could serve as idealizations of the various objects studied by observational astronomers, concepts endowed with the various properties that come under consideration in empirical work. Our hope is that combined with a number of refinements, which future work will undoubtedly introduce, the formulas deduced and the methods developed will contribute to a better understanding of the universe.

The goal so outlined is of necessity very distant. In its definitive form it would involve a "stochastization" of the relativistic, now deterministic, cosmology. In particular, this would imply consideration of stochastic processes in non-Euclidean spaces. Our own studies are limited to Euclidean space.

2. BASIC IDEAS

In order that the stochastic model of the realm of the galaxies can serve as a tool in empirical cosmological studies, it must be concerned explicitly with those objects that are under study, that is, galaxies and clusters of galaxies. Furthermore, the model should be general enough to include several possibilities that are currently under consideration and, perhaps, are subjects of disputes. These disputes may be exemplified by the difference of opinions regarding the law of redshift. According to the majority of writers, the redshift of galaxies represents a Doppler effect and means velocity with which galaxies and clusters recede from the observer. Contrary to this, others, for example, Zwicky [23], assert that the universe is essentially static and that the redshift reflects some, thus far unknown, phenomenon. Thus, in order to be useful in the possible resolution of the dispute, the stochastic model constructed should offer possibilities that the universe may be static or expanding. Another example of a difference in opinions is Zwicky's assertion [25] that "clusters of clusters" of galaxies do not exist. This is contrasted with the opinions of Abell [2] and of de Vaucouleurs [24] that clusters of galaxies are themselves clustered. Thus, in order to be useful, the model of the realm of the galaxies must allow for the possibility of "superclustering."

Finally, many astronomers take it for granted that clusters of galaxies are stable systems. This is contrasted with the opinion of Ambartsumian [3] and his school, at least partly supported by several other astronomers such as E. M. and G. R. Burbidge [5], that at least some of the clusters expand, perhaps explosively. To be adequate, the mathematical tool for studying such questions must involve room for instability of clusters of galaxies, etc.

Considerations of the above kind dictate a number of assumptions of mathematical character about what is happening in space. However, the observations that are being made now, and also the majority of those that may be made in the future, cannot yield direct information about the happenings in space. These observations are and must remain limited to what a photographic plate taken with an optical telescope, or a tape connected with a radiotelescope, etc., may be capable of recording. However powerful the source of light or of radio signals, if it is sufficiently far from the observer, it will not be observed. Also, depending upon the vagaries of the photographic plates and other instruments of observation, the same source of light may be observed tonight but fail to be observed tomorrow. Finally, depending on the physiological state of the observer, the same photographic plate viewed by an observer on one occasion may result in his noticing certain details which are not noticed on another occasion. Table 1 illustrates this point [9]. It represents the results of two counts of images of galaxies on the same photographic plate. Both counts were made by the same astronomer, one of the most experienced in this kind of work. The second set of counts was made some time after the first. For purposes of counting, the plate was divided into $36 \times 36 = 1296$ small squares and the figures in the main body of Table 1 represent the numbers of those squares in which the first count gave the number of images of galaxies indicated at the bottom of the column and the second count the number of images indicated in the left end of the corresponding row of the table.

It is seen that, on many occasions, the images of galaxies counted on the second count were not those counted on the first and

Table 1. Correlation between two systems of counts of images of galaxies by the same observer on the same photographic plate.

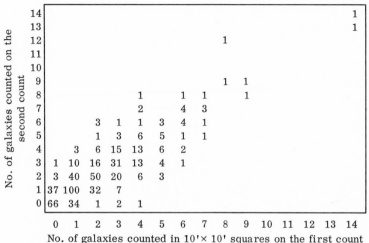

No. of galaxies counted on the second count (vertical axis) vs. No. of galaxies counted in 10'× 10' squares on the first count (horizontal axis).

Second count \ First count	0	1	2	3	4	5	6	7	8	9	10	11	12	13	14
14															1
13															1
12									1						
11															
10															
9									1	1					
8					1		1	1		1					
7					2		4	3							
6			3	1	1	3	4	1							
5			1	3	6	5	1	1							
4		3	6	15	13	6	2								
3	1	10	16	31	13	4	1								
2	3	40	50	20	6	3									
1	37	100	32	7											
0	66	34	1	2	1										

vice versa.

These and similar other observations indicate that, to be realistic, the model of the realm of the galaxies must include a second category of stochastic assumptions. This second category must be concerned with the relationship between what is happening in space and what is observed on the earth. Naturally, these assumptions must refer specifically to each set of instruments used for observations.

3. BASIC ASSUMPTIONS

We begin with the assumptions of the first category, those relating to happenings in space.

In the model, the galaxies are idealized as dimensionless particles whose actual distribution in space is treated as a single realization of a stochastic process. In accordance with the so-called "cosmological principle" representing an extrapolation of the Copernican idea that the earth is not the center of the universe, this stochastic process is postulated to be stationary in the three spatial coordinates and possibly stationary in the fourth, time coordinate. More specifically, it is assumed that for any moment in time the space distribution of galaxies is that of nth order clustering. The process of nth order clustering is defined recursively. We begin with zero order clustering, as follows.

(i) To every region R in space (really a Borel set) there corresponds a random variable $\alpha(R)$ representing the number of particles in R. This variable $\alpha(R)$ is capable of assuming non-negative integer values 0, 1, 2, ...

(ii) The set function α is countably additive.

(iii) If R_1 and R_2 are congruent, then $\alpha(R_1)$ and $\alpha(R_2)$ have the same distribution.

(iv) If R_1, R_2, ..., R_s, ... are disjoint, then the corresponding $\alpha(R_i)$ are mutually independent.

It follows that the distribution of $\alpha(R)$ depends only on the Borel measure m(R) of R and that the probability generating function of $\alpha(R)$ must be of the form, say,

(1) $G_{\alpha(R)}(t) = E[t^{\alpha(R)}] = \exp[h(t) m(R)]$,

where

(2) $h(t) = -h_0 + \sum_{k=1}^{\infty} h_k t^k$

with

(3) $h_k \geq 0$,   and $\sum\limits_{k=1}^{\infty} h_k = h_0 > 0$.

In other words, the distribution of $\alpha(R)$ must be an infinitely divisible distribution.

In order to define the process of clustering of order $n + 1$, we assume that nth order clustering has been already defined and proceed as follows.

Let particles C be distributed in nth order clustering. These particles will be termed centers of clusters of order $n + 1$.

(v) With each particle C there is connected an integer-valued non-negative random variable $\nu_{n+1}(C)$ representing the number of cluster members centered at C.

(vi) The random variables $\nu_{n+1}(C_1)$, $\nu_{n+1}(C_2)$, ... corresponding to different cluster centers are mutually independent and identically distributed. Their common p.g.f. is denoted by

(4) $g_{n+1}(t) = E(t^{\nu_{n+1}})$.

(vii) Given that $\nu_{n+1}(C) = m$, there are m particles $\pi_1^{(n+1)}, \pi_2^{(n+1)}, \ldots$
..., $\pi_m^{(n+1)}$ attached to the cluster center C. Let $(X_1^{(k)}, X_2^{(k)}, X_3^{(k)})$
$= X^{(k)}$ stand for the coordinates of $\pi_k^{(n+1)}$ and $(u_1, u_2, u_3) = u$ for coordinates of C. It is assumed that, given u, all the m triplets $X^{(k)}$ are random variables that are mutually independent and identically distributed. The distribution of $X^{(k)}$ is assumed to have a probability density, say

(5) $f_{n+1}(x - u) = f_{n+1}\left\{ \left[\sum\limits_{i=1}^{3} (x_i - u_i)^2 \right]^{1/2} \right\}$,

depending only on the distance between the point $x = (x_1, x_2, x_3)$ and the center of the cluster C. The function f_{n+1} is described as the "structure" of the $(n + 1)$st order cluster.

Naturally, the functions g_k and g_m and also f_k and f_m may well be different for $k \neq m$.

This completes the definition of $(n + 1)$st order clustering.

Apart from a few remarks, all that follows will refer to clustering of the first order.

4. FUNDAMENTAL FORMULA FOR CLUSTERING OF FIRST ORDER

Consider some particles π distributed in three-dimensional Euclidean space with clustering of first order. Also consider an arbitrary number s of disjoint regions (Borel sets) $R_1, R_2, ..., R_s$. The subject of this section is the joint distribution of the numbers of some of the particles π that fall in the regions R_i. However, because of a great variety of different applications, it is not the total number of particles π in R_i that will be the subject of our discussion.

For each region R_i we shall consider a certain chance trial T_i supposed to be performed independently for each particle $\pi \in R_i$. The definition of the trial T_i may well vary from one region R_i to the next. Each such trial is supposed to be capable of producing one of some $m_i + 1$ different and mutually exclusive outcomes, with probabilities $\theta_{ij}(x)$ that may depend on the coordinates $x = (x_1, x_2, x_3)$ of the particle π considered, $j = 1, 2, ..., m_i + 1$, with

(6) $\qquad \sum_{j=1}^{m_i+1} \theta_{ij}(x) = 1.$

It is assumed that the functions $\theta_{ij}(x)$ are measurable.

The first m_i of the possible outcomes of T_i will be described as "successes." The $(m_i + 1)$st outcome will be termed "failure."

The subject of our interest in this section is the random variables α_{ij}, representing numbers of those particles in R_i that "have the jth success," for $i = 1, 2, ..., s$ and $j = 1, 2, ..., m_j$. A single boldface letter $\boldsymbol{\alpha}$ will symbolize the set of all these variables and a single boldface letter $\mathbf{t}$ will stand for the corresponding arguments t_{ij} of the probability generating function of $\boldsymbol{\alpha}$. The formula giving this function is termed the fundamental formula for first order clustering [11]. It is

(7) $\qquad G_{\boldsymbol{\alpha}}(t) = \exp\left(\int h\left\{g_1\left[1 - \sum_{i=1}^{s} \sum_{j=1}^{m_i} (1 - t_{ij})p_{ij}(u)\right]\right\} du\right).$

Here the integral in the exponent extends over the whole three-dimensional space. This integral may well be divergent to $-\infty$, in which case all the variables α_{ij} have infinite values with probability one. The symbol $p_{ij}(u)$ denotes the conditional probability, given $u = (u_1, u_2, u_3)$, that a particle from a cluster centered at u will be found in R_i and that it will have the jth success. Thus

(8) $\qquad p_{ij}(u) = \int_{R_i} \theta_{ij}(x)f(x - u)\, dx.$

Clustering of first order possesses the following very convenient property.

Theorem 1. Whatever be the function h(t) defined by (2) and (3), and whatever be the probability generating function $g_1(t)$, there exists a positive number λ and a probability generating function g(t), such that g(0) = 0 and such that, for all $|w| \leqq 1$,

(9) $h[g_1(w)] = -\lambda[1 - g(w)]$.

This theorem implies that, without loss of generality, it can be assumed that zero order clustering is a Poisson process with expected number of particles per unit volume equal to λ, and that all first order clusters contain at least one particle, so that $P\{\nu_1 \geqq 1\} = 1$. Using this theorem the fundamental formula (7) can be rewritten as

(10) $G_\alpha(t) = \exp\left(-\lambda \int \left\{1 - g\left[1 - \sum_{i=1}^{s} \sum_{j=1}^{m_i} (1 - t_{ij})p_{ij}(u)\right]\right\} du\right).$

Remark 1. More recent studies indicate the necessity of distinguishing at least three different types of clusters of galaxies: compact, medium compact and loose. Accordingly, to treat problems relating to the different varieties of clusters, it is necessary to postulate three different "structures" of clusters.

Remark 2. It is easy to see how formula (10) can be used to deduce an analogous formula for clustering of second order [18], etc.

The use of the fundamental formula (10) will be illustrated below.

5. HYPOTHESES REGARDING THE POSSIBLE EXPANSION OF THE UNIVERSE

All the above considerations, including formula (10), refer to a fixed moment in time, or as it is picturesquely described, to the "world map." If the universe is static, then the world map will correspond to the "world picture." This will also be the case if, as postulated by Bondi, Gould and Hoyle [4], the universe is actually expanding but the local density of matter in all of its forms is maintained constant by continuous creation of new matter. On the other hand, if the universe is expanding and no new matter is created, then the world picture observed from the earth must differ from the world map. The reason is that the light and radio signals from galaxies observed on earth today took quite some time, actually hundreds of millions of years, to reach the earth. As a result, the present day world picture is a mixture of what happened last year, at close distances from us, with what happened two years ago at double the first distance, etc., with what happened millions of years ago at very large distances. And, if the expansion of the universe is a reality and no new matter is being created, then millions of years ago the density of matter must have been greater than it is now.

In the model that we consider, the possible expansion of the universe is treated deterministically [12]. Namely, the requirement of stationarity of the distribution of cluster centers at any given moment implies that the deterministic motions of these centers must be such that, at each moment t, the radial velocity, say $v(t)$, of a cluster center be proportional to the distance $D(t)$ of this cluster center, so that

(11) $v(t) = D(t)H(t),$

where $H(t)$ is a function time. If the redshift z of galaxies really represents the Doppler effect of the expansion velocities, then the redshift multiplied by c, the velocity of light, will be equal to $v(t)$ and we shall have

(12) $cz(t) = D(t)H(t)$.

Formulas taking into account (11) are fairly complicated and will not be reproduced here. For purposes of further development it should be stated that the tentative estimates of distances of galaxies for which the redshift z has been measured (mostly by M. Humason and N. U. Mayall [7]) suggest that over some half-billion years in the past the function $H(t)$ did not change very much. Thus, as a first approximation, we assume that $H(t)$ is a constant H, namely, the so-called Hubble constant. In this way, the average redshift of several galaxies belonging to the same cluster is an estimate of the cluster's radial velocity and thereby of the cluster's distance $D(t)$ multiplied by the constant H. The value of H continues to be a subject of study but it is believed to be of the order of 100 km/sec/Mpc.

Whether the redshift is a Doppler effect of the velocity of expansion or not, we take it that, in the above sense, it is a distance indicator for the clusters of galaxies.

6. MORPHOLOGICAL TYPES OF GALAXIES AND THEIR LUMINOSITIES

The origin of the different morphological types of galaxies is a mystery. However, mere inspection of Figures 1 and 2 suggests that an elliptical galaxy is an object qualitatively different from a spiral. Thus, it is appropriate to study the several morphological types separately. Without entering into the details of the problem, we shall consider that there are several, say T, different morphological types and that the acquisition by a given galaxy of any t-th morphological type, t = 1, 2, ..., T, is a chance event with a determined probability, say λ_t. One of the questions that is now under broad discussion is whether λ_t depends on the type of cluster and on the number ν of its members. Specifically, it is frequently asserted that while spiral galaxies are quite frequent in small clusters and also in large open clusters, they are extremely scarce in rich compact clusters. Incidentally, taking this assertion for granted a theory of the origin of elliptical galaxies has been proposed, according to which the elliptical galaxies are a result of collisions of the originally spiral galaxies. In compact clusters such collisions are expected to occur more frequently than in loose clusters and they are expected to destroy the structure of the spiral objects and to transform them into elliptical galaxies.

In the following we shall consider the application of the fundamental formula (10) to the study of frequency of morphological types. For this purpose it will be tentatively assumed that the morphological type of one galaxy is independent of that of any other and that, at least for clusters of a specified type, it is independent of all other variables of the system.

The brightness of a galaxy is measured by the so-called absolute magnitude $\mathfrak{M}$. This is a decreasing linear function of the logarithm of the amount of radiation emitted by the source per unit of time and passing through a unit area perpendicular to the direction of radiation and placed at 10 units of distance from the source of light.

The absolute magnitude of galaxies is not directly observable. The related directly observable quantity is the apparent magnitude μ connected with the absolute magnitude by the relation

(13) $\mu = \mathfrak{M} - 5 + 5 \log_{10} D + \chi(z)$

where D is distance and the last term represents the dimming due to various reasons. One reason is the absorption of light by dust and gas clouds between the galaxy and the observer. Another source of dimming is the loss of energy of light due to redshift. For very large distances, that is for very large values of z, the dimming term χ is substantial. However, for selected areas in the sky and for the categories of galaxies for which a substantial amount of observations are available it is quite small [7]. The further developments reported in this paper neglect the last term in (13).

In the model studied, the absolute magnitude $\mathfrak{M}$ is considered as a random variable independent of all other random variables in the system. It is admitted that, for each given morphological type t of galaxies, $\mathfrak{M}$ has a probability density designated by $P_{\mathfrak{M}}(M \mid t)$. This density is called the "luminosity function" of the galaxies of type t and is an important subject of theoretical as well as of empirical studies.

The difficulty of empirical studies of the frequency of morphological types and of the luminosity functions is connected with the fact that, whatever the available instrumentation, it is always of limited power and, as a result, the data that may be collected for study are always subject to selection: Those galaxies that appear faint either because they are intrinsically faint or because they are extremely distant, escape observation.

In order to study the luminosity function of galaxies using any empirical data, it is unavoidable to adopt some specific hypotheses regarding the chance mechanism behind the decision to include a given galaxy in an observational program. The hypothesis adopted in our work [15], [17] is as follows:

(ix) For a fixed morphological type t of galaxies, the probability that a galaxy will be included in the catalogue depends on the value of the galaxy's apparent magnitude m and on nothing else. The probability in question is denoted by $\Phi(m,t)$ and called selection probability.

It is quite certain that hypothesis (ix) is not exactly true for any kind of observations now available. For example, the astronomer studying a given cluster of galaxies is likely to expend much more energy and time observing faint galaxies than we would when dealing with a galaxy in the field. Nevertheless, there are indications that for separate categories of galaxies and for certain kinds of observations, notably for observations of redshift, hypothesis (ix) is reasonably realistic.

Adopting hypothesis (ix), we use the fundamental formula to evaluate the so-called "catalogue distribution" of apparent magnitude, the "catalogue distribution" of absolute magnitude and the "catalogue abundance" of the various types of galaxies. The "catalogue distribution" of any random characteristic X of a galaxy is defined as the conditional distribution of that variable, given that the galaxy in question has been included in a given catalogue. Generically, the unconditional probability density of characteristic X will be denoted by $p_X(x)$. This will be termed the "space" distribution of X. The "catalogue" counterpart of $p_X(x)$ will be marked with an asterisk, $p_X^*(x)$. The same notation will be used for the various derived concepts. Thus $E^*(X)$ will mean the conditional expectation of X given that the galaxy has been included in the catalogue. It will be termed the "catalogue" expectation of X, etc. The general line of study is as follows. Using a catalogue of galaxies, it is possible to study empirically the catalogue distributions of the various characteristics of galaxies. If the catalogue distributions of these characteristics are connected with the space distributions, then the catalogue distributions, with the relevant formulas, can be used to study the space distributions which are the natural ultimate subjects of interest.

7. MORPHOLOGICAL TYPES AND LUMINOSITY FUNCTIONS IN SPACE AND IN THE CATALOGUE

Consider a catalogue of galaxies compiled over a region R in the sky, where the same letter R will denote the corresponding solid angle with its vertex at the observer. We suppose that for each galaxy the catalogue gives its morphological type, its apparent magnitude and its redshift. The latter two variables, combined with the value of the Hubble constant, yield the distance of the galaxy and its absolute magnitude. Considered as a random variable, the distance will be denoted by Ξ. The particular value of Ξ will be denoted by ξ.

Let N_t denote the random variable representing the total number of t-type galaxies in the catalogue and n_t the observed value of N_t. Also let $\Sigma N_t = N$ and $\Sigma n_t = n$. The double subscript ti will refer to the ith galaxy of morphological type t in the catalogue, for t = 1, 2, ..., T and i = 1, 2, ..., N_t. The subjects of our study in this section are the joint distribution of the random variables $N_1, N_2, ..., N_T$ and, for a fixed t, the catalogue distribution of n_t pairs of variables (μ_{ti}, Ξ_{ti}), the apparent magnitude and distance of the ith galaxy belonging to type t. The method of using the fundamental formula is as follows:

Select an arbitrary set of n positive different numbers $\xi_1, \xi_2, ..., \xi_n$ and a number $\Delta > 0$ sufficiently small for the n intervals $[\xi_i, \xi_i + \Delta)$ to be disjoint. Next let R_i denote that part of the solid angle R for which $\xi_i \leq \xi < \xi_i + \Delta$, for i = 1, 2, ..., n. Also we shall use the letter

R_0 to denote the set of all those points of R that do not belong to any of the regions R_1, R_2, ..., R_n. Thus, the regions R_0, R_1, ..., R_n will be disjoint and their union will be R.

Now it will be convenient to renumber the regions R_1, ..., R_n by ascribing to each a pair of subscripts ti for t = 1, 2, ..., T and i = 1, 2, ..., n_t. This is done arbitrarily using the fact that $\Sigma n_t = n$.

The next step is to select n arbitrary real numbers m_{ti} for t = 1, 2, ..., T and i = 1, 2, ..., n_t and a small positive number δ. For each region R_{ti} we define the jth "success" of a galaxy as follows: (i) the galaxy has the jth morphological type; the probability of this is λ_j for j = 1, 2, ..., T; (ii) the apparent magnitude of the galaxy is between the limits $m_{ti} \leqq \mu < m_{ti} + \delta$; (iii) the galaxy is included in the catalogue. Obviously, the probability $\theta_{tij}(x)$ of the jth success in the region R_{ti} is

(14) $\theta_{tij}(x) = \lambda_j p_{\mathfrak{M}}(m_{ti} + 5 - 5 \log_{10} \xi \mid t) \Phi(m_{ti}, m_{tij}) \delta + o(\delta)$

(15) $p_{tij}(u) = \int_{R_{ti}} f(x - u) \theta_{tij}(x) dx.$

For the region R_0 only one kind of success is defined: a galaxy falling in R_0 is successful if it is included in the catalogue, irrespective of its morphological type and apparent magnitude.

With this specialization of the regions and of successes, the fundamental formula determines the probability, say $P(n,\xi,m)$, of the following compound event: (a) the number of galaxies successful in R_0 is equal to zero; (b) the number of galaxies having success number t in R_{ti} is equal to unity; (c) the number of galaxies in R_{ti}

having any other kind of success defined for that region is equal to

zero. This same compound event may be described differently: (α)

the catalogue contains exactly n galaxies; (β) of these n galaxies ex-

actly n_t belong to type t, for t = 1, 2, ..., T; (γ) the ith galaxy of type

t has its distance Ξ and its apparent magnitude μ between limits

(16)
$$\xi_{ti} \leqq \Xi < \xi_{ti} + \Delta$$
$$m_{ti} \leqq \mu < m_{ti} + \delta.$$

A similar application of the fundamental formula determines an-

other probability which we shall denote simply by P(n). This is the

probability that the region R will contain exactly n galaxies in-

cluded in the catalogue, irrespective of their distances and magni-

tudes. The quotient $P(n,\xi,m)/P(n)$ is then the conditional probability,

given that the catalogue contains exactly n galaxies, that n_t of

them will be of type t, for t = 1, 2, ..., T and that they will be at the

indicated distances and that they will have the indicated apparent

magnitudes. Finally, dividing this conditional probability by a

numerical factor representing the number of different ways the n

galaxies can be assigned the indicated properties, and also by $(\delta\Delta)^n$

and passing to the limit as $\delta \to 0$ and $\Delta \to 0$, we obtain the condi-

tional joint probability density of the n pairs of variables μ and Ξ,

each pair relating to a particular galaxy of a specified type.

Without making any assymption regarding G_ν, the result of the

operation described is extremely messy and hardly useable. How-

ever, the result becomes simple and very useful if one gives credence to the astronomers' ability to identify, perhaps with occasional mistakes, the so-called "field galaxies." This term is used to designate those galaxies that form "clusters" composed of just one element. For these clusters $\nu = 1$ and, consequently, $G_\nu(t) \equiv t$. For field galaxies the described use of the fundamental formula leads to the following conclusions.

Theorem 2. Given that a catalogue contains exactly n field galaxies, the conditional distribution of the numbers N_t of those field galaxies that belong to the morphological type t, for t = 1, 2, ..., T, have a multinomial distribution with the probability generating function

(17) $$G_N^*(v_1, v_2, ..., v_T) = \left(\sum_{t=1}^{T} \lambda_t^* v_t \right)^n,$$

where λ_t^* stands for the "catalogue abundance" of morphological type t, connected with the corresponding space abundance λ_t by the formula

(18) $$\lambda_t^* = \frac{\lambda_t I_t J_t}{\sum_{i=1}^{T} \lambda_i I_i J_i},$$

where, for t = 1, 2, ..., T,

(19) $$I_t = \int_{-\infty}^{+\infty} \Phi(m,t) e^{3m/a} \, dm,$$

(20) $$J_t = \int_{-\infty}^{+\infty} p_{\mathfrak{M}}(M \mid t) e^{-3M/a} \, dM.$$

Here $a = 5 \log_{10} e$. It is seen that, given a catalogue of field galaxies, containing a total N galaxies of all types, N_t of which are of type t, the catalogue abundance λ_t^* can be consistently estimated by the quotient N_t/N. Then, if the selection probabilities $\Phi(m,t)$ and the luminosity functions $p_{\mathfrak{M}}(M \mid t)$ of all the types are known, formulas (18), (19) and (20) will lead to consistent estimates, say $\hat{\lambda}_t$ of the space abundances λ_t. In a further section, certain numerical results regarding these estimates will be given.

Theorem 3. <u>Given that a catalogue contains a fixed number</u> n <u>of field galaxies with subdivision according to types, the absolute magnitude</u> $\mathfrak{M}$ <u>and the apparent magnitude</u> μ <u>of each such galaxy in the catalogue form a pair of random variables that is independent from all other similar pairs. Furthermore,</u> $\mathfrak{M}$ <u>and</u> μ <u>corresponding to the same galaxy are mutually independent.</u> Their catalogue densities for any type t are, respectively,

$$(21) \qquad p_\mu^*(m \mid t) = I_t^{-1} \, e^{3m/a} \, \Phi(m,t),$$

$$(22) \qquad p_{\mathfrak{M}}^*(M \mid t) = J_t^{-1} \, e^{-3M/a} \, p_{\mathfrak{M}}(M \mid t).$$

Particular cases of these formulas have been known for quite some time [22] and used in stellar statistics. The usual restrictive assumption used in the deduction of the formulas was that the catalogue studied is complete up to a certain fixed limiting magnitude, say m^*. In the present terminology this is equivalent to assuming that the selection probability Φ is equal to unity for $m < m^*$ and to zero otherwise. Occasionally, it was also assumed that the luminosity function has some particular specified form, for example that it is a normal density.

As given, formulas (21) and (22) are remarkable for their simplicity and unexpectedness. The first of them indicates that, if the classification of morphological types is fine enough for the selection probability $\Phi(m,t)$ to depend upon the apparent magnitude and t, and on nothing else, then this selection probability is determined by the catalogue distribution of the apparent magnitude, at least up to a multiplicative constant. If the catalogue is compiled with an intention to achieving completeness, understood to mean an effort to include all field galaxies in the region R sufficiently bright for convenient observation, then it may be taken for granted that $\Phi(m,t)$ is close to unity for "bright" values of m. This assumption, combined with formula (21), provides an estimate of $\Phi(m,t)$. This, in turn, yields an estimate of the integral I_t needed in formula (18).

Formula (22) is also remarkable because it indicates that, for any given type t, the catalogue distribution of the absolute magnitude of field galaxies is independent of the selection factor $\Phi(m,t)$. However, it does not coincide with the corresponding space distribution! In order to appreciate this result it is interesting to visualize two astronomers, one working with a 200-inch telescope and the other using a modest 20-inch telescope. These astronomers may well agree on a division of labor, one concentrating on rather faint and the other on bright field galaxies. For these two astronomers the selection probabilities will be strikingly different. Yet, formula (22) asserts that, apart from random sampling variation, the data collected by the two astronomers will show the same distribution of absolute magnitude.

Formula (22) yields an unambiguous estimate of the luminosity function as follows

$$(23) \qquad p_{\mathfrak{M}}(M \mid t) = c p_{\mathfrak{M}}^*(M \mid t) e^{3M/a},$$

where c is a norming constant. An interesting implication of formula (23) is that, if $M_1, M_2, \ldots, M_{n_t}$ are the absolute magnitudes of n_t field galaxies of type t in a given catalogue, then an unbiased estimate of the space mean absolute magnitude is obtained by averaging not the numbers M_i themselves but rather the products $M_i e^{3M_i/a}$. In fact, formula (23) implies that for any measurable function $\Psi(M)$ the space expectation of $\Psi(\mathfrak{M})$ is equal to the product of the norming constant c in (23) by the catalogue expectation of the product $\Psi(\mathfrak{M}) e^{3\mathfrak{M}/a}$, so that

$$(24) \qquad E[\Psi(\mathfrak{M})] = c E^*[\Psi(\mathfrak{M}) e^{3\mathfrak{M}/a}].$$

In particular, putting $\Psi \equiv 1$, it is seen that the integral J_t needed in formula (18) is the reciprocal of the norming factor c and can be estimated by the weighted mean of $e^{3M_i/a}$ with catalogue frequencies of the various values of M as weights.

8. GALAXIES IN CLUSTERS AND IN THE FIELD

The purpose of the present section is to illustrate the method by which the above results can be used in order to verify certain assertions frequently made regarding cluster galaxies and field galaxies. One of these assertions is that while spirals are quite frequent in the field, in small groups and in large open clusters, exemplified by the Virgo Cluster, they are very rare or non-existent in compact clusters. The difficulty is that the assignment of galaxies to different types of clusters is confounded with distance. Small groups of galaxies are familiar predominantly at short distances. Also the open Virgo Cluster is relatively near. On the other hand, the distance of the nearest large compact cluster, the Coma Cluster, is about five times that of the cluster in Virgo. Thus, the galaxies of a given absolute magnitude located in compact clusters are generally fainter than those known in small groups and in Virgo Cluster. If it happens that selection probabilities for any two morphological types of galaxies are sharply different, then this would affect the catalogue abundances of these types among galaxies of distant compact and the nearby open clusters and groups. This situation is further complicated by the circumstance that thus far there is no certainty that the luminosity functions of the same types of galaxies in clusters coincide with those of field galaxies. A direct solution of the problem of comparing the membership of a given type of cluster with that of other clusters or with field galaxies requires the estimation of corresponding selection probabilities and luminosity functions. Unfortunately, for cluster galaxies no formulas exist as simple as formulas (21) and (22) from which the selection probabilities and luminosity functions could easily be determined. Thus, the direct method of comparing the type composition and the luminosity functions of cluster galaxies presents difficulties. However, an indirect method to attain a partial solution of the problem is available through the use of the results described in the preceeding section.

This method depends upon the availability of a catalogue of galaxies, giving their apparent magnitudes and redshift, about which one could be confident that the selection probabilities $\Phi(m,t)$ are the same for field galaxies and for cluster galaxies. The catalogue data for field galaxies could then be used to estimate these selection probabilities, as well as the luminosity functions of the various morphological types, and their space abundances λ_t. Finally, using the distance D of a given cluster, as estimated through the mean redshift of its members in the catalogue, one could compute the expected percentage of each morphological type among those members of the clusters that are to be found in the catalogues, on the extra assumption that the luminosity functions of cluster members are the same as those of field galaxies. If the expected percentages so computed are comparable to those actually observed in the catalogue, then this would be an indication not only that the abundances of the different morphological types in clusters are similar to those in the field, but also that the corresponding luminosity functions do not differ very much. On the other hand, a sharp disagreement between the predicted percentages and those observed would indicate only that either the type abundances or the luminosity functions (or both) for cluster galaxies are not the same as for galaxies in the field.

Unfortunately, at the present time no source of data seems to be available insuring that the selection probabilities for cluster galaxies are the same as those for field galaxies. The HMS catalogue, which provides the bulk of data for field galaxies, is based on observations by Humason, who used the giant 200 inch Hale telescope on Mt. Palomar, and by Mayall, to whom only the modest 36 inch Crossley telescope was available at the Lick Observatory. Thus, the selection probabilities based on the totality of data reflect a combination of potentialities offered by these two very different instruments and also, possibly, a combination of personal preferences of the two observers. This does not apply to clusters more distant than the Virgo and the Coma clusters. Here, the observations of redshift are due to a number of other astronomers whose attention became attracted by particular clusters. For example, the totality of observations of redshift for members of the cluster of galaxies No. 2199 in Abell's catalogue is due to Rudolf Minkowski [10], who became interested in it because of the presence of a strong radio source. A priori it would appear rather unlikely to find Minkowski's selection probabilities similar to the combination of those of Mayall and Humason while they were observing field galaxies. Finally, even though the redshift data for Coma Cluster were obtained by Mayall and Humason in almost equal shares, one would expect that in dealing with the Coma Cluster they would be inclined to spend more time and effort to observe faint objects than they would do when working on field galaxies.

In spite of these considerations indicating that the method of comparing cluster galaxies and field galaxies as outlined above is not applicable to the data available, the necessary computations were actually performed. The goal was: to use the HMS data on field galaxies (following Sandage [7], some of the small group members were treated as if they were field galaxies) in order to predict the proportions of the eight morphological types among catalogued cluster galaxies and to compare these predictions with proportions in the catalogues. The expected sharp differences between predictions and the catalogue data would be an indication that either space abundances of types or the luminosity functions in clusters (or both) are not comparable to those for field galaxies. The calculations included all clusters and groups for which redshift observations are available for at least 3 members. Because of small numbers of observations for groups of galaxies and for clusters more distant than the Coma Cluster, predictions and also observations for these systems had to be combined. All the details of the study are not yet published, but some information is given in [8], [16], [20]. Table 2, page 166, gives a summary.

The first column gives numbers n_t of field galaxies in the HMS catalogue belonging to the various cosmological types. The next column gives the estimated space abundances. The subsequent five

Table 2. Percentage of Galaxies of Different Morphological Types

Morphological Type	Field Galaxies HMS n_t	Field Galaxies Space $\lambda\%$	Near Groups n = 32 Exp.	Near Groups n = 32 Obs.	Virgo n = 80 Exp.	Virgo n = 80 Obs.	Intermediate Groups n = 72 Exp.	Intermediate Groups n = 72 Obs.	Coma n = 46 Exp.	Coma n = 46 Obs.	"Far" Clusters n = 48 Exp.	"Far" Clusters n = 48 Obs.
EO–E3	83	3.7	7.0	6.2	10.6	12.5	18.1	22.2	34.8	34.8	44.1	47.9
E4–E7,Ep	28	7.6	5.3	9.4	5.0	15.0	6.2	9.7	8.8	19.6	12.3	8.3
SBO,SBa	21	2.2	4.1	9.4	5.6	10.0	4.6	13.9	2.3	0.0	1.1	2.1
SBb	26	1.9	3.4	3.1	5.0	2.5	6.3	4.2	7.8	2.2	5.8	0.0
SO,SOp	66	11.5	12.5	6.2	13.7	15.0	16.1	23.6	20.5	28.3	21.0	14.6
Sa,Sap,Sab	51	3.3	7.1	12.5	11.2	8.8	11.6	11.1	8.8	8.7	4.3	18.7
Sb,Sbc	77	20.8	21.8	12.5	20.6	12.5	17.5	8.3	11.0	2.2	8.0	6.2
Sc,Scp,SBc	94	49.0	38.8	40.6	28.5	23.8	19.5	6.9	5.9	4.3	3.3	2.1
Correlation coefficient				0.90		0.73		0.32		0.88		0.90

double columns give the predicted and then the observed percentages of each morphological type in two clusters, Virgo and Coma,
and in three combinations of systems for which the data for only a
few objects were available. Here "near groups" means several
small groups of galaxies all nearer than the Virgo Cluster. "Intermediate groups" means small groups with distances between those
of the Virgo and the Coma clusters. "Far clusters" means several
clusters beyond Coma, up to and including the Corona Borealis
Cluster. This category includes the cluster Abell 2199 studied by
Minkowski.

The effect of increasing distance is clearly visible in the trends
of predicted percentages of the particular morphological types.
Thus, for example, for the morphological type E0-E3, with the estimated space abundance of only 3.7%, the expected catalogue frequencies in the various systems climb steadily from 7.0 percent
in the "near groups" to 44.1 percent in the "far clusters." This
increase in predicted catalogue frequencies is due to the fact that
the galaxies concerned are intrinsically very bright and, besides,
to that for a fixed apparent magnitude their estimated selection
probabilities are greater than those for other morphological types.
On the other extreme, the predicted catalogue frequencies of the
abundant spirals Sc, Scp, SBc, for which the selection probabilities are low, fall off from 38.8 percent to 3.3 percent. It will be
seen that the frequencies of these types actually observed parallel
closely the predictions.

While the agreement between the predictions and the observations for the two extreme types could hardly be any better than it is, this agreement for some other types is not good. For example, the predictions for Sb, Sbc are systematically too large and much too large. However, the trend of predictions parallels that of observations, suggesting that, through the unavoidable chance variation, the obtained value of λ is an overestimate. Similar remarks apply to the morphological types E4-E7, Ep.

Because of the various reservations described earlier in this section, the content of Table 2 came as a considerable surprise. While the same reservations prevent us from considering this table as documentary evidence, it does suggest that the scarcity of spiral galaxies in compact clusters, such as Coma, may be only an apparent scarcity. In actual fact, the spiral galaxies may be just as frequent in Coma as they are in Virgo or in the field, and the impression of scarcity of spirals in Coma and the impression that this cluster is dominated by ellipticals may be due solely to the difference in the relative difficulty of observations. It would be most interesting to obtain data so collected as to insure the sameness of selection probabilities for cluster galaxies and for field galaxies. Then the problem of comparing the two categories could perhaps be solved with less uncertainty than on the basis of the calculations just described.

9. THE PROBLEM OF INTERLOCKING OF CLUSTERS OF GALAXIES

The purpose of the present section is to give an illustration of the use of the fundamental formula (10) in a problem whose general character is radically different from that described above.

While the content of astronomers' studies appears to justify fully the construction of the process of clustering as a model of the distribution of galaxies in space, the possibility must be considered that the many observational astronomers preoccupied with clusters of galaxies are mistaken and that the entities that are called "clusters" are not isolated systems but merely local condensations in an essentially continuous field of galaxies. The following picturesque description may give an intuitive idea of the general problem.

One possible role of clusters may be described by comparing them with a great number of balloons, perhaps released at a festivity. However large the number of these balloons may be, they will appear as distinct bodies floating separately. A picture contrary to this is that of a volume of suds in a bubble bath. Here the particular clusters of galaxies are compared with particular bubbles. The question is to decide which of the two pictures fits the real situation better.

We must begin by reformulating the problem so that it acquires a mathematical meaning. One of the several possibilities examined [12], [14] is as follows.

Consider a particular cluster C_0 of galaxies with a fixed center, perhaps at the origin of coordinates. This cluster will be called the selected cluster. According to the theory considered, the selected cluster has a random number ν_0 of members. Suppose ν_0 has assumed a value n > 1. We shall number the n galaxies of the selected cluster in decreasing order of their distance, say η, from the center. Thus

(25) $\eta_1 \geqq \eta_2 \geqq \ldots \geqq \eta_n \geqq 0.$

The distances η_i are random variables whose joint distribution is calculable from the structure of clusters $f(x - u)$. Now consider some cluster C_1 of galaxies other than C_0. Let Γ be a galaxy belonging to this cluster C_1.

Definition 1. We shall say that Γ penetrates the selected cluster to the depth k if Γ is interior to a sphere centered at the center of C_0 having its radius equal to η_k.

Definition 2. We shall say that the cluster C_1 penetrates the selected cluster to the depth k if at least one galaxy of the cluster C_1 penetrates C_0 to the depth k.

It will be noticed that the penetration to the depth k of the cluster C_0 by the galaxy Γ from the cluster C_1 is a random event with the following elements of randomness.

(i) The number ν_0 of members in C_0 is random.

(ii) Given $\nu_0 = n \geqq k$, the radius η_k is random.

(iii) The position of the center of the cluster C_1 is random.

(iv) The number ν_1 of members of C_1 is random.

(v) Given the center of C_1 and the value of ν_1, the locating of the ν_1 members of C_1 are random.

Now we define a random variable, say ξ_k, whose distribution is calculable from the fundamental formula and may be taken as a characteristic of the degree to which the clusters of galaxies are interlocked.

Definition 3. <u>The symbol ξ_k stands for the number of those clusters C_1 that penetrate the selected cluster to the depth k.</u>

The motivation for considering the variable ξ_k is easy to appreciate. For example, suppose that the estimates for all the elements in the model of clustering indicate that the probability that ξ_1 exceeds zero is of the order of magnitude of one in a thousand. This finding would favor the comparison of clusters of galaxies with balloons: it is only in exceptional cases that a cluster C_1 penetrates any selected cluster to the depth unity. On the other hand, if the empirical findings indicated that $P\{\xi_{10} > 0\}$ is a sizeable number, then this would be an indication that "clusters" of galaxies as isolated systems are a fiction and that the process of clustering is no more than an interpolatory structure to be abandoned just as soon as something more realistic or more convenient to handle is invented.

It should be mentioned that calculations of numerical values of probabilities relating to ξ_k were performed using the first tentative estimates of the various elements of first order clustering. The figures so obtained [14] indicated very considerable frequencies of interpenetration of clusters. However, it was later found that the original estimates of the elements of first order clustering were unrealistic, their inaccuracy being due to our lack of information regarding the random character of counts of galaxies as exhibited in Table 1. As things stand now, the question as to whether the clusters of galaxies resemble balloons or suds is still open.

For the purposes of this section it is essential that the probability generating function G_{ξ_k} of ξ_k, for any $k > 0$, with an additional natural assumption that the selected cluster contains at least $N \geqq k$ galaxies, is calculable from the fundamental formula (10). Unfortunately, while simple, the deduction of G_{ξ_k} takes some space and some discussion. The interested reader is referred to the publication [12] which includes all the necessary details.

Acknowledgement. It is a pleasure to express my indebtedness to Professor Gérard de Vaucouleurs and to Professor Rudolf Minkowski for allowing me to use their excellent photographs reproduced in Figures 1, 2, and 3.

REFERENCES

1. Abell, George O.: "The distribution of rich clusters of galaxies," Astrophys. J. Suppl. **3** (1958) pp. 211-288.

2. _____ : "Evidence regarding second-order clustering of galaxies and interactions between clusters of galaxies," Astron. J., **66**, (1961) pp. 607-613.

3. Ambartsumian, V. A.: "Instability phenomena in systems of galaxies." Astron. J. **66** (1961) pp. 536-540.

4. Bondi H.: Cosmology. Cambridge University Press, 1952.

5. Burbidge, E. M. and G. R.: "Recent investigations of groups and clusters of galaxies." Astron. J. **66** (1961), pp. 541-550.

6. Hubble, E. P.: The Realm of the Nebulae. Oxford University Press, 1936.

7. Humason, M., Mayall, N. U. and Sandage, A. R.: "Redshift and magnitudes of extragalactic nebulae." Astron. J. **61** (1956), pp. 97-162.

8. Marcus, A.: "Precisions of the estimates relating to the selection factor of galaxies." Astron. J. **67** (1962), pp. 580-581.

9. Mayall, N. U., Scott, E. L. and Shane, C. D.: "Statistical problems in the study of galaxies." Bull. Intern. Stat. Institute. **37** (1960), pp. 35-53.

10. Minkowski, R.: "NGC 6166 and the cluster Abell 2199." Astron. J. **66** (1961), pp. 558-561.

11. Morgan, W. W. and Mayall, N. U.: "A spectral classification of galaxies." Publ. Astron. Soc. Pacific **69** (1957), pp. 291-303.

12. Neyman, J.: "Sur la théorie probabiliste des amas de galaxies et la vérification de l'hypothèse de l'expansion de l'univers." Ann. Inst. Henri Poincaré **14** (1955), pp. 201-244.

13. Neyman, J. and Scott, E. L.: "A theory of the spatial distribution of galaxies." Astrophys. J. **116** (1952), pp. 144-163.

14. _____ : "Frequency of separation and of interlocking of clusters of galaxies." Proc. Nat. Acad. Sci. **39** (1953), pp. 737-743.

15. _____ : "Large scale organization of the distribution of galaxies." Handbuch der Physik, **53** (1959), pp. 416-444.

16. _____ : "Estimation of the dispersion of the redshift of field galaxies." Astron. J. **66** (1961), pp. 148-155.

17. _____ : "Field galaxies: luminosity, redshift and abundance of types." Proc. Fourth Berkeley Symposium on Math. Stat. and Probability, **3**, pp. 261-276. University of California Press, Berkeley 1961.

18. Neyman, J., Scott, E. L. and Shane, C. D.: "On the spatial distribution of galaxies. A specific model." Astrophys. J. **117** (1953), pp. 92-133.

19. _____ : "Statistics of images of galaxies with particular reference to clustering." Proc. Third Berkeley Symposium Math. Stat. and Probability, **3**, pp. 75-111. University of California Press, Berkeley, 1956.

20. Neyman, J., Scott. E. L. and Zonn, W.: "Abundances of morphological types among galaxies in clusters and in the field." Astron. J. **67** (1962), p. 583.

21. Page, T. L.: "Average masses of double galaxies." Proc. Fourth Berkeley Symposium on Math. Stat. and Probability, **3**, pp. 277-306. University of California Press, Berkeley, 1961.

22. Trumpler, Robert and Weaver, Harold. "Statistical Astronomy." University of California Press, Berkeley 1957.

23. Vaucouleurs, G. de: "Classification and morphology of external galaxies." Handbuch der Physik, **53** (1959), pp. 275-310.

24. _____ : "Recent studies of clusters and superclusters." Astron. J. **66** (1961), pp. 629-632.

25. Zwicky, R.: Morphological Astronomy, Springer, Berlin, 1957.

26. Zwicky, F., Herzog, E. and Wild, P.: Catalogue of Galaxies and of Cluster of Galaxies. Vol. 1. Publication of the California Institute of Technology, Pasadena, 1961.

Physical Models in Mathematics

JAN MYCIELSKI
University of California
Berkeley, California
and Wroclaw University, Poland

ABSTRACT

This talk was devoted to pointing out the problem of how the intuitive evidence of the consistency of the Zermelo-Fraenkel set theory (ZF) arises. In fact, it seems that our common belief in a kind of existence of the natural models of ZF (which gives an evidence of the consistency of ZF) is based on a physical model. On the other hand, another theory other than ZF, which is obtained by replacing the axiom of choice by the axiom of determinateness, seems to agree with the physical model better than ZF, nevertheless we are not convinced of its consistency.

(Copyright © 1963 by Prentice-Hall, Inc.)

Mathematical Models in Statistical Mechanics

MARK KAC
The Rockefeller Institute
New York, N. Y.

ABSTRACT

A one-dimensional gas of hard rods with exponential attraction described by the potential $\alpha\gamma \exp(-\gamma x)$ has been previously discussed by the author. The present talk reports some further results obtained in collaboration with Uhlenbeck and Hemmer. In particular, the limit $\gamma \to 0$ leads to the van der Waals equation of state including the Maxwell equal area rule below the critical point. The interplay between the mathematical methods and physical intuition was stressed.

(Copyright © 1963 by Prentice-Hall, Inc.)

On Constraints in Classical Fields

STEFAN DROBOT
University of Notre Dame
Notre Dame, Indiana

The purpose of this talk is to present an unified description of various physical systems. The unifying idea consists in defining a physical system by the constraints introduced into the principle of virtual displacements, and by the Lagrange multipliers corresponding to those constraints. Let me illustrate this idea by examples.

1. STATICS OF A RIGID SYSTEM OF POINTS

Such a system is defined in the following way. In an Euclidean space referred to some coordinate system we consider, e.g., N points with their position given by the radius-vectors $\vec{x}_a$, $\vec{x}_b$, the indices a, b, identifying the points. Let $\delta\vec{x}_a$, $\delta\vec{x}_b$ be the variations of $\vec{x}_a$, $\vec{x}_b$, i.e., the virtual displacements of the points. The physical description of such a system contains the following four points.

(Copyright © 1963 by Prentice-Hall, Inc.)

A. External Factors. Here, they are external forces acting on the points of the system. These forces are defined as vectors $\vec{F}_a$ such that $\vec{F}_a \delta \vec{x}_a$ is a scalar, specifically here, work. The external factors are given in advance.

B. Constraints. Here, they consist in that the system is rigid, i.e., that the variations satisfy the condition

(1.1) $\delta[(\vec{x}_a - \vec{x}_b) \cdot (\vec{x}_a - \vec{x}_b)] = 0$

for every pair of points a, b. It is well known that for a rigid system this condition is equivalent to the following one: Fix one point, e.g., b, then there exists a vector $\delta \vec{\omega}$ independent of a and b, such that

(1.2) $\delta(\vec{x}_a - \vec{x}_0) - \delta \vec{\omega} \times (\vec{x}_a - \vec{x}_0) = 0.$

The constraints, thus, are equations in variations $\delta \vec{x}$.

C. Response of the System to the Constraints. Here, they are reactions of the rigid system. They are defined as the Lagrange multipliers $\vec{\lambda}_a$ to the constraints, to be introduced into

D. The Principle of Virtual Work. In the example considered the principle requires that

$$\sum_a \{\vec{F}_a \delta x_a + \vec{\lambda}_a [\delta(\vec{x}_a - \vec{x}_0) - \delta \vec{\omega} \times (\vec{x}_a - \vec{x}_0)]\} = 0$$

for arbitrary $\delta \vec{x}_0$ and $\delta \vec{\omega}$.

Hence, the well-known conditions of equilibrium of such a rigid system follow, viz.,

$$\sum_a (\vec{F}_a + \vec{\lambda}_a) = 0, \quad -\sum_a \vec{\lambda}_a = 0, \quad \sum_a \vec{\lambda}_a \times (\vec{x}_a - \vec{x}_0) = 0.$$

2. STATICS OF STRINGS, RODS AND SHELLS

Let $\vec{x}(a)$ with a continuous parameter a be a one dimensional continuum. The external forces $\vec{f}(a)$ acting on it are given functions such that $da\,\vec{f}(a)\,\delta\vec{x}(a)$ is the elementary virtual work. If the constraints are analogous to (1.1), i.e.,

$$(2.1) \qquad \frac{d\delta\vec{x}}{da} \cdot \frac{d\vec{x}}{da} = 0,$$

the system is a model of a string which is able to react in the direction of its tangent only. The only scalar-valued Lagrange multiplier $T(a)$ is the tension. The principle of virtual work, viz.,

$$\int da \left(\vec{F}\delta\vec{x} + T\frac{d\vec{x}}{da} \cdot \frac{d\delta\vec{x}}{da} \right) + \text{terms on the boundary} = 0$$

yields, by integrating by parts, in view of the arbitrariness of $\delta\vec{x}$, the equilibrium equation of the string:

$$\vec{F} - \frac{d}{da}\left(T\frac{d\vec{x}}{da} \right) = 0$$

with appropriate boundary conditions. If the constraints are analogous to (1.2), i.e.,

$$(2.2) \qquad \frac{d\delta\vec{x}}{da} - \delta\vec{\omega} \times \frac{d\vec{x}}{da} = 0, \quad \frac{d\delta\omega}{da} = 0$$

we have a model of a rod, which is able to react with an internal vector-valued force $\vec{\lambda}$, defined as the Lagrange multiplier to the first constraint, and with internal, continuously distributed couples $\vec{\mu}$, defined, as in (2.2), as the vector-valued multiplier to the second constraint in (2.2).

The principle of virtual work

$$\int da \left[\vec{F}\delta\vec{x} + \vec{\lambda}\left(\frac{d\delta\vec{x}}{da} - \delta\vec{\omega} \times \frac{d\vec{x}}{da}\right) + \vec{\mu}\frac{d\delta\vec{\omega}}{da} \right] + \cdots = 0$$

yields now the equilibrium equations of a rod:

$$\vec{F} - \frac{d\vec{\lambda}}{da} = 0, \qquad \vec{\lambda} \times \frac{d\vec{x}}{da} - \frac{d\vec{\mu}}{da} = 0.$$

Now, let $\vec{x}(a^1, a^2)$, with two continuous parameters a^1, a^2, be a two-dimensional continuum (surface). Let

$$g_{ij} = \partial_i\vec{x} \cdot \partial_j\vec{x}, \qquad i, j = 1, 2,$$

where $\partial_i = \partial/\partial a^i$, be the metric tensor of that surface, i.e.,

$$d\vec{x} \cdot d\vec{x} = g_{ij}da^i da^j,$$

summation convention assumed.

If the constraints are analogous to (1.1), i.e.,

$$\delta(d\vec{x} \cdot d\vec{x}) = 0$$

whence

(2.3) $\delta g_{ij} = \partial_i\delta\vec{x} \cdot \partial_j\vec{x} + \partial_i\vec{x} \cdot \partial_j\delta\vec{x} = 0,$

then we have a model of a membrane theory of shells. Namely, let $\vec{f}(a^1, a^2)$ be external force such that $da^1 da^2 \sqrt{g}\,\vec{f}\,\delta\vec{x}$, with $g = \det g_{ij}$, is the virtual work on the surface element. The Lagrange multipliers λ^{ij} to the constraint (2.3) represent the stress-tensor T^{ij} in the membrane, symmetric by its very definition:

$$T^{ij} = \lambda^{ij} + \lambda^{ji}.$$

The principle of virtual work

$$\iint da^1 da^2 \sqrt{g}\,(\vec{f}\delta\vec{x} + T^{ij}\partial_i\delta\vec{x}\partial_j\vec{x}) + \cdots = 0$$

yields the equations of equilibrium of a membrane

$$\sqrt{g}\vec{f} - \partial_i(\sqrt{g}\,T^{ij}\partial_j\vec{x}) = 0.$$

This can also be written as

$$f^j - \nabla_i T^{ij} = 0$$

where ∇_i denotes the covariant derivative with respect to the metric tensor g_{ij} of the surface.

If the constraints are analogous to (1.2), i.e.,

$$d\delta\vec{x} - \delta\vec{\omega}\times d\vec{x} = 0, \qquad \partial_i\delta\vec{\omega} = 0$$

we obtain the moment-theory of shells. I will omit the detailed calculations of this.

3. HYDROSTATICS

Let $\vec{x}(a^1, a^2, a^3)$ be a 3-dimensional continuum situated in a 3-dimensional Euclidean space. Assume that the constraints are formally the same as in (2.3), analogous to (1.1), i.e., $\delta g_{ij} = 0$. This means that the virtual displacement δx_i is a Killing vector, satisfying the condition

(3.1) $\qquad \nabla_i \delta x_j + \nabla_j \delta x_i = 0, \qquad i, j = 1, 2, 3.$

If the Lagrange multiplier corresponding to this constraint is λ^{ij}, denote

$$p^{ij} = \lambda^{ij} + \lambda^{ji}.$$

If f^i is the external force acting on volume elements, then the principle of virtual displacements

$$\iiint da^1 da^2 da^3 \sqrt{g}\,(f^i \delta x_i + p^{ij}\nabla_j \delta x_i) + \cdots = 0$$

gives the equations of equilibrium of a continuous medium:

$$\sqrt{g}\,f^i - \nabla_j(\sqrt{g}\,p^{ij}) = 0 \qquad (i = 1, 2, 3)$$

with appropriate boundary conditions stemming from the dotted $(\ldots)$ part of the variational principle. The p^{ij} is the stress tensor.

The hydrostatics of a non-viscous fluid can be obtained by assuming the constraints in the form

(3.2) $\delta\sqrt{g} = 0$

which can be transformed into

$$\sqrt{g}\,g^{ij}\delta g_{ij} = 0.$$

Denote the scalar-valued Lagrange multiplier by p. Then, the principle of virtual work gives

$$\sqrt{g}\,f_i - \nabla_i(\sqrt{g}\,p) = 0$$

thus, the equations of hydrostatics, with p interpreted as pressure.

4. DYNAMICS OF A MATERIAL POINT

Let $\vec{x}(a^0)$ be a one-dimensional continuum situated in a 4-dimensional space. The parameter a^0 is interpreted as a "local" time τ, in some interval $\tau_1 \leqslant \tau \leqslant \tau_2$. Denote

$$g_{\infty} = \partial_\tau \vec{x} \cdot \partial_\tau \vec{x}$$

and assume that the constraint is $\delta g_{00} = 0$. If the components of the four-vector $\vec{x}$ are $x^0, x^i, i = 1, 2, 3$, with x^0 interpreted as the time-coordinate, t, and x^i as the spatial coordinates, the constraint is

(4.1) $\partial_\tau t \cdot \partial_\tau \delta t + \partial_\tau x_i \cdot \partial_\tau \delta x^i = 0.$

Denote the scalar-valued Lagrange multiplier corresponding to this constraint by m. Then the principle of virtual displacement is

$$\int_{\tau_1}^{\tau_2} d\tau \left[F_0 \delta t + F_i \delta x^i + m(\partial_\tau t \cdot \partial_\tau \delta t + \partial_\tau x_i \cdot \partial_\tau \delta x^i) \right] + \cdots = 0$$

where F_0, F_i, $i = 1, 2, 3$, is the external factor. Integration by parts yields

(4.2)
$$F_0 - \partial_\tau(m\partial_\tau t) = 0$$
$$F_i - \partial_\tau(m\partial_\tau x_i) = 0$$

with some boundary conditions stemming from the dots (...).

If the 4-dimensional space is Galilleo-Euclidean, i.e., if

$$\partial_\tau t = 1$$

then the last three equations in (4.2) are the Newton's equations of the motion of a material point, while the first equation shows that F_0 is to be interpreted as the source of the changeable mass m.

If the 4-dimensional space is a Lorentz-Minkowski one, i.e., if

$$\partial_\tau t = \sqrt{1 - (v/c)^2}$$

we obtain the relativistic dynamics of a material point.

5. HYDROMECHANICS

Let now $\vec{x}(a^0, a^1, a^2, a^3)$ be a 4-dimensional continuum situated in a 4-dimensional Galileo-Euclidean space. Let the parameter a^0 be interpreted as a local time τ, and let the a^i, $i = 1, 2, 3$ identify the particle (Lagrange coordinates). Let x^0 be the time coordinate t of the particle, and x^i its spatial coordinates; thus $\partial_\tau t = 1$, and $\partial_\tau x^i = v^i$ (velocity). Denote

$$g_{\alpha\beta} = \partial_\alpha x^\gamma \cdot \partial_\beta x_\gamma$$

with the Greek indices running over $0, 1, 2, 3$ (summation convention) and assume that the constraints are analogous to (1.1), i.e., that

(5.1) $\partial_\alpha x^\gamma \cdot \partial_\beta \delta x_\gamma + \partial_\alpha \delta x^\gamma \cdot \partial_\beta x_\gamma = 0.$

Let the corresponding Lagrange multipliers be $T^{\alpha\beta}$. If the external factor is acting on 4-volume element $da^0 da^1 da^2 da^3 \sqrt{g}$, with $g = \det g_{\alpha\beta}$ and such that $F^\gamma \delta x_\gamma$ is a scalar, then the principle of virtual work yields the equations

$$F^\gamma - \partial_\alpha (T^{\alpha\beta} \partial_\beta x^\gamma) = 0 \qquad (\gamma = 0, 1, 2, 3).$$

By denoting $T^{00} = \rho$, $T^{ij} = p^{ij}$ and assuming $T^{0i} = \rho v^i$, we get for $\gamma = 0$

$$(5.2) \qquad F^0 = \partial_t \rho + \partial_i (\rho v^i)$$

thus, the continuity equation. For $\gamma = i = 1, 2, 3$ and assuming $a^i = x^i$ we obtain the Euler's equations of hydromechanics, in a generalized form,

$$F^i - (F^0 + v^i F^0 - \partial_\tau \rho) = \rho(\partial_t v^i + v^j \partial_j v^i) - \partial_j p^{ij}$$

in which the 0-th equation has been taken into account. Thus, ρ is the density, F^0 the intensity of the sources of matter, and p^{ij} is the tensor of the pressure.

If the space $\vec{x}$ has a Lorentz-Minkowski metric, we would obtain the equations of relativistic hydromechanics.

6. HYDRO-ELECTROMAGNETIC FIELD

Consider now, more generally that the constraints of a 4-dimensional continuum situated in a 4-dimensional space, are not of the type (1.1) as in (5.1) but of the type (1.2), i.e., we have

$$(6.1) \qquad \nabla_\alpha \delta x_\beta - \epsilon_{\alpha\beta}{}^{\lambda\mu}(\nabla_\lambda \delta \omega_\mu - \nabla_\mu \delta \omega_\lambda) = 0$$

where ∇_α denotes the covariant derivative with respect to the metric $g_{\alpha\beta}$ in the space considered, $\epsilon^{\alpha\beta\lambda\mu}$ is the antisymmetric

Ricci tensor, and $\delta\omega_\lambda$ is an arbitrary vector. Let the Lagrange multipliers corresponding to the constraints be

(6.2) $T^{\alpha\beta} = P^{\alpha\beta} + F^{\alpha\beta}$

where $P^{\alpha\beta}$ is the symmetric, and $F^{\alpha\beta}$ the antisymmetric part. If F^α represents the external factor, the principle of virtual displacement yields, by integrating per parts the following equations of the field

(6.3)
$$F^\alpha - \nabla_\beta(P^{\alpha\beta} + F^{\alpha\beta}) = 0 \qquad (\alpha = 0,\ 1,\ 2,\ 3)$$
$$\epsilon^{\alpha\beta\lambda\mu}\nabla_\lambda F_{\alpha\beta} = 0 \qquad (\mu = 0,\ 1,\ 2,\ 3).$$

If we assume that $T^{\alpha\beta}$ is symmetric, thus $F^{\alpha\beta} = 0$, we get again the equations of hydromechanics. If $T^{\alpha\beta}$ is antisymmetric, thus $P^{\alpha\beta} = 0$, the equations (6.3) are of the Maxwell's type, $F_{\alpha\beta}$ being interpreted as the electromagnetic tensor. The external factor F^α is, in usual notation, the 4-vector $F^\alpha = (4\pi/c)S^\alpha$, with $S^\alpha = (ic\rho,\ j^1,\ j^2,\ j^3)$, $\vec{j}$ being the electrical current, ρ the charge-density. If both symmetric $P^{\alpha\beta}$ and antisymmetric part $F^{\alpha\beta}$ do not vanish, equations (6.3) give a model of a hydro-electromagnetic field.

7. GRAVITATION

The model of a gravitational field can be obtained by considering the following two constraints:

(7.1) $\delta g_{\alpha\beta} = 0$ and $\delta\int d\Omega\sqrt{g}\,R$

where R denotes the scalar curvature of the 4-space Ω considered.

Let $T^{\alpha\beta}$ be the Lagrange multiplier corresponding to the first constraint in (7.1) and κ the scalar-valued multiplier corresponding to the second constraint. Thus, the principle of virtual work is now

(7.2) $\int d\Omega \sqrt{g}\, T^{\alpha\beta} \delta g_{\alpha\beta} + \int d\Omega \kappa \delta(\sqrt{g}\, R).$

The second integrand can be transformed into

$$\sqrt{g}\, \kappa \left(R^{\alpha\beta} - \frac{1}{2} g^{\alpha\beta} R \right) \delta g_{\alpha\beta}$$

where $R^{\alpha\beta}$ is the Einstein symmetric tensor.

If we consider the left-hand side expression in (7.2) as functional over the metric $g_{\alpha\beta}$, then the $\delta g_{\alpha\beta}$ are arbitrary and (7.2) gives

(7.3) $T^{\alpha\beta} + \kappa \left(R^{\alpha\beta} - \frac{1}{2} g^{\alpha\beta} R \right) = 0.$

These are Einstein equations of gravitational field, $T^{\alpha\beta}$ being interpreted as the energy-matter tensor, and κ as the gravitational constant.

Since

$$\nabla_\alpha \left(R^{\alpha\beta} - \frac{1}{2} g^{\alpha\beta} R \right) = 0$$

equation (7.3) is in agreement with the first equation in (6.3) provided $F^\beta = 0$.

DISCUSSION

Uhlenbeck: In the case of the gravitational equation what is the external factor?

Drobot: It has not been introduced here because the integral in the principle of virtual work was considered as a functional over the metric tensor $g_{\alpha\beta}$, and not over the δx's.

Uhlenbeck: Do you have the gravitational equations for the empty gravitational field?

Drobot: Yes, if you assume $T^{\alpha\beta} = 0$.

Kruskal: Since you get both fluid equations and electro-magnetic equations out of the same formalism could you put them together and get the equations for magneto-hydrodynamics?

Drobot: This is done in equation (6.3).

Kruskal: Does this include the treatment with self-consistent fields where the outside terms F^{α} are actually produced by the fluids themselves?

Drobot: No. For instance, the component F^{0} in (5.2) should be interpreted as an external source of matter. Usually the continuity equation in hydromechanics is written without F^{0}.

Friedrichs: If you interpret those ρ's and $\vec{j}$'s that you had in your F^{α} expressed in terms of the Maxwell field you automatically get the wave equation. I mean the Dirac wave equation, the relativistic wave equation.

Drobot: The δx's are not considered here as operators but "ordinary" vectors.

Friedrichs: You deal here with the classical model.

Grad: To get the complete system for magneto-hydrodynamics there is just one equation missing in the macroscopic theory, and that is "Ohm's law". Do you know how to get that?

Drobot: The "Ohm's law", which is of the same type as in viscous fluids the relationship between the pressure and rate of deformation is an additional assumption not introduced explicitly into this scheme. It can be done afterwards. Let me make one more comment which I should have done at the beginning of my talk. In Ulam's

recent book* he writes: "The usual introduction of the continuum

leaves much to be discussed and examined critically... There are,

therefore, constraints on the class of possible motions which are

not explicitly recognized."

*S. M. Ulam, A Collection of Mathematical Problems, Interscience Publishers, Inc., 1960, Reading, Mass., pp. 89 and 90.

List of
Participants

F. J. Belinfante   Purdue University, Lafayette, Indiana

Kenneth M. Case   University of Michigan, Ann Arbor, Michigan

Richard H. Dalitz   University of Chicago, Chicago, Illinois

J. J. DeSwart   Fermi Institute, University of Chicago, Chicago, Illinois

Stefan Drobot   University of Notre Dame, Notre Dame, Indiana

Freeman J. Dyson   Institute for Advanced Study, Princeton, New Jersey

Kurt O. Friedrichs   New York University, New York, N.Y.

Harold Grad   New York University, New York, N.Y.

Rudolf Haag   University of Illinois, Urbana, Illinois

Carl Iddings   University of Chicago, Chicago, Illinois

Walter R. Johnson   University of Notre Dame, Notre Dame, Indiana

Mark Kac   Rockefeller Institute, New York, N.Y.

Martin D. Kruskal   Princeton University, Princeton, New Jersey

George C. Kuczynski   University of Notre Dame, Notre Dame, Indiana

Lawrence Lee   University of Notre Dame, Notre Dame, Indiana

Ruey-Wen Liu   University of Notre Dame, Notre Dame, Indiana

John L. Magee   University of Notre Dame, Notre Dame, Indiana

Cecil B. Mast   University of Notre Dame, Notre Dame, Indiana

Edward G. McShane   University of Virginia, Charlottesville, Virginia

Charles J. Mullin   University of Notre Dame, Notre Dame, Indiana

Jan Mycielski   University of California, Berkeley, California;
                Wroclaw University, Poland

Czeslaw Ryll-Nardzewski   University of California, Berkeley,
                          California; Wroclaw University, Poland

Roger G. Newton   Indiana University, Bloomington, Indiana

Jerzy Neyman   University of California, Berkeley, California

Louis Pierce   University of Notre Dame, Notre Dame, Indiana

George Y. Rainich   University of Notre Dame, Notre Dame, Indiana

Arnold E. Ross   University of Notre Dame, Notre Dame, Indiana

Frederick D. Rossini   University of Notre Dame, Notre Dame,
                       Indiana

Peter Seibert   University of Notre Dame, Notre Dame, Indiana

Elizabeth L. Scott   University of California, Berkeley, California

Harrison Shull   Indiana University, Bloomington, Indiana

Hugo Steinhaus   University of Notre Dame, Notre Dame, Indiana;
                 Wroclaw University, Poland

Adolph G. Strandhagen   University of Notre Dame, Notre Dame,
                        Indiana

Ludwig Tewordt   University of Notre Dame, Notre Dame, Indiana

George E. Uhlenbeck   Rockefeller Institute, New York, N.Y.

Stanislaw M. Ulam   University of California, Berkeley, California

Paul A. Viebrock   University of Notre Dame, Notre Dame, Indiana

Norman J. Zabusky   Bell Telephone Laboratory, Whippany, New Jersey

Antoni Zygmund   University of Chicago, Chicago, Illinois